A Brighter Life

solving the puzzle called cancer

A Brighter Life

solving the puzzle called cancer

Gabriel Lightfriend

STARLIGHT BOOKS ~ BELLINGHAM, WASHINGTON

A Brighter Life

Publisher:
Starlight Books
Bellingham Washington

Editor: Dorene Carrel
Book Design and composition: Chris Molé
Cover Design: Jordan Ekdahl
Printed by: Premier Graphics, Bellingham, Washington

Library of Congress Cataloging-in Publication Data
Lightfriend, Gabriel

Flowers of Light / Gabriel Lightfriend
1st ed. p. cm.
ISBN 13   978-0-9790029-1-5
ISBN 10   0-9790029-1-5

Printed and bound in the United States of America
First edition 10 9 8 7 6 5 4 3 2 1

Ye are all the children of the light,
and the children of the day: we are
not of the night, nor of darkness.

Thessalonians, 5-5

ACKNOWLEDGMENTS

This book would have been impossible were it not for the dedication and compassion of selfless healers such as Rene Caisse, Dr. Charles Brusch and Elaine Alexander. I would also like to offer a special thanks to those individuals and organizations who assisted with this project, namely Jordan Ekdahl for graphic design, Dorene Carrel for editing, Chris Molé for book layout, Carmen Tamayo and Diane Robert for research on Flor·essence, Leda Fair for testimonial support, Bev Maya for flow chart data compiled on Flor·essence and Disease Progression, Hal Gunn, co-founder and CEO of Inspire Health, the American Cancer Society and the American Botanical Council.

CONTENTS

INTRODUCTION

Cancer is a topic that has been researched and written about to no end, yet it remains a pandemic threat that continues to haunt the mental fabric and faith of human beings everywhere. Who will be its next victim? Which family might one day have to endure the wrath of its aggressive and unpredictable temperament?

In 2008, it is estimated over 1.4 million Americans will be diagnosed with some form of cancer and around 560,000 will die from this disease. Current annual projections in Canada indicate 160,000 new cases will surface, resulting in 72,000 deaths. Throughout the world the statistics are alarming and most of us know of a loved one or friend who has struggled helplessly against this dreaded nemesis.

It doesn't seem that long ago when my own mom passed away from pancreatic cancer. The circumstances surrounding the ordeal proved to be an experience I will never forget:

A few weeks before her 61st birthday, Mom became overwrought with abdominal pain and was taken to the doctor for x-rays and other tests. A biopsy was subsequently performed and when the results came back, her doctor gave her approximately six months to live. It was mid-October, and since I was living 3,000 miles away at the time, I patiently waited for further updates and decided to drive back over the Christmas holidays. Around the latter part of November, I learned that Mom's condition had quickly deteriorated. She was not only weak and bed-ridden, but couldn't keep any food down, resulting in a noticeable loss of weight. Apparently, the tumor had grown so massive it blocked her digestion and she was sent to the hospital for an operation. When the surgeons opened her up, they noticed the cancer had also spread to her liver and other organs. Upon hearing this news, I immediately jumped in my car and started my journey out west. After driving for sixteen hours, I encountered a mild winter storm and made a brief stop to check in with the family. It was quite a shock when I was informed that Mom's status was now critical and that she might only have a handful of days to live. It all happened so fast. I continued speeding across the country, the weather mounting into a fierce blizzard as I traversed the Prairies and Canadian Rockies. Apart from the side effects of chemotherapy and morphine injections, Mom developed pneumonia and water had seeped into her lungs. She knew I was coming and was heaving and hyperventilating, hanging on with all her might as I desperately sped onward. The heating system in my car had failed and I remember shivering under a wool blanket. I drove frantically while peering through a small clearing on the now ice-coated windshield. As fate would have it, my car broke down two hundred miles from the hospital and Mom passed away before I even had the chance to see her.

Perhaps that stressful journey sixteen years ago compelled me to write this book. Perhaps I might prevent the happening of a similar fate from tearing the hearts of others confronted with the confusing cloud that often infiltrates accounts with cancer. Dealing with cancer is difficult enough as it is, and even though medical technology has improved vastly over the past decade, conventional treatment with radiation or chemo-therapy is still often described as a living nightmare.

I am overwhelmed by the volumes of people who donate exorbitant funds to cancer research or place their fidelity on some "dangling carrot" of a cure that may never come to fruition. Cancer remains a problematic puzzle much too complex to ever pinpoint in any precise fashion. No matter how ingenious, the latest breakthrough can never cure the underlying causes.

One can choose to see cancer as an evil entity that science needs to subdue, or as "nature's omen," motivating us to re-evaluate the toxic manner in which we conduct our life.

Cancer, like any progressive disease, just doesn't happen out of the blue. Emotional stress, environmental poisons and poor dietary habits slowly exert a negative influence on our health. According to the National Soft Drink Association, consumption of carbonated soft drinks in the United States has grown to over 600 twelve ounce servings per person per year. And Americans lead the world in ice cream consumption, with an estimated twenty-two quarts per person per year. These are just a few of the hundreds of packaged and prepared foods people habitually indulge in—items saturated with sugar, fat or chemical preservatives. The majority of illnesses in the twentieth and twenty-first centuries are self-inflicted, and the responsibility lies with each individual to find a balanced way of living.

To prevent or to overcome an existing cancer takes a well-spring of willpower, resourcefulness and loving support. There is no need to retreat into a silent internal suffering when there are so many welcoming hands anxious to assist. There is no need to carry the world on our shoulders when we all must share in the workload of nurturing a family, conducting a business or improving the planet. And there is no need to remain a prisoner to all of our nagging thoughts and fears when life presents a bountiful platter of experiences in the present moment.

There are many positive steps we can take to instill health and harmony back into our lives. *A Brighter Life* sheds light on some of the many options available through the portrait of a typical family as they come together to solve one member's encounter with cancer. Although the story is fictional, much of the script presented is based on personal experience or factual data acquired through research and discovery. Informative websites, inspirational books, rejuvenating remedies and a life-enhancing stream of natural healing modalities are waiting to make us whole. As we learn to flow with the journey, the miracles we seek will unfold.

The Good Old Days

Childlike wonder is the portal to happiness.

There was a time when the sun was my good friend—a warm beam of love in an endless sky. There was a time when children such as I were blessed with innocence. The gripping fear of two world wars was over and a peaceful enthusiasm enveloped the land. Families were young and dazzled by dreams that promised a brighter future. My parents struggled financially, but any hint of poverty was offset by their rich kindness and a home that provided a secure sanctuary. One could often find me enchanted for hours playing with an assortment of toys or conversing with some imaginary companions—a wide-eyed child who only knew that life was beautiful.

I was a small little squirt with a short crew-cut and a serene countenance that cast an impression of some reclusive monk. At the age of six I attended public school and my universe expanded. The first grade was filled with a curriculum of fun activities. Crafts were created from crayons, paper, scissors or glue, and finger painting was as much fun as it was messy. Characters from simple storybooks sprang to life and friends were found through the variety of schoolyard games we shared. By the end of the first semester my shyness hadn't prevented me from interacting with most of the kids in the neighborhood and we were anxious to explore the adventures of summer.

It was odd how we seemed to merge in the local park, as if we were all somehow synchronized. There was invariably a game in progress we could freely join in. Red Rover, Hide-And-Seek and Capture The Flag were everybody's favorite. As I scampered out the door I could hear my mom's reminder, "Vincent, don't go too far and let your sister play too!"

"I promise," came the soft reply. I heeded her concerned advice and always kept my word.

My sister Willow was a year younger. Her freckled complexion and gapped-toothed smile gave her a tame appearance, but she was as nimble as a wild deer. She often excelled at Tag and those contests where speed was a decided advantage. My short legs were no match for Willow's lean frame.

"Tag, you're it! You can't catch me, I'm the Gingerbread Man!" she teased.

"You can run, you can run, as fast as you can!" the others chanted.

There were a few lads slower than me, but I was often the bull in a ring of matadors chasing some elusive shadows. The thrill of inching closer but evading the tag was more important for them than any concept of winning. Somewhere in my gene pool I must have inherited some persistent DNA, for eventually I charged out and nipped a shirt sleeve or pant leg and freed myself from the dilemma of being the pursuer. We frolicked until the sun descended and the calling of concerned parents was heard like the whistles of referees signaling the game was over.

We lived in a quiet town perched on the banks of the Fraser River. Its muddy shores were flanked by lumber mills, fishing vessels and canneries that oftentimes saturated the air with a disturbing stench. We hid indoors then, while my father was off at work in one of the factories. We always referred to him as Dad, but Jude was a strong, athletic gentleman sporting size thirteen shoes that were determined to leave their footprint on whatever path they pursued. He always dressed conservatively in plain white cotton shirts and khaki trousers, although his relentless work ethic gained admiration from the many European and Japanese laborers. Everyone was content just to have an income and retreat home to their families after the workday whistle blew, while Dad kept his shirt sleeves rolled-up and spent many evenings upgrading his education at night school. When he graduated a few years later, he quickly found new avenues of employment. To celebrate his next new job, he splurged on his first car. The old blue Chevy proudly rolled along the simple streets of Steveston as we all waved to the locals. The speed limit was only twenty mph in those days. However, having your very own set of wheels was much more convenient than hitchhiking for a ride or waiting around for a bus. Either way, we never seemed to be in that much of a hurry, but now we indulged in frequent trips to the country to pay a visit to my grandmother.

Granny had a monstrous mansion that was built to accommodate her five children, but they had since moved out and married to start a life of their own. Except for her, the antique furniture and the many species of indoor plants she nurtured, the house was empty. It was a strange sensation being stationed in such a big house, so we wandered around her colorful gardens and tiny orchard. There was this giant apple tree in her backyard that I loved the best. Its wrinkled trunk and swirling branches were home to thousands of emerald leaves—leaves that sparkled in the noonday sun, providing camouflage for the hidden treasure of lush, golden apples. In these early years, the tree occupied the center of my tiny kingdom. I remember the countless games we played beneath its fruitful boughs. "Who's afraid of the Big Bad Wolf, Big Bad Wolf? Who's afraid of the Big Bad Wolf? Tra La La La La."

The little kids who joined in from across the street quivered while I sang the words. The Big Bad Wolf had to guess the item that each participant secretly chose. Sometimes the category was animals, vegetables, fruit or colors. When I correctly guessed their secret choice, the victim had to race around the apple tree and back to home base before I could catch them. If someone was tagged, they fell down paralyzed and their time was up—they were out of the game. It was a safe and fascinating world back then. Little did we realize the Big Bad Wolf was a foreshadow of events yet to come.

If we weren't playing games, we assisted Granny with the gardens by plucking out weeds or pruning the shrubs. She taught us the patient skills required to become a novice gardener, and it was enlightening to witness the array of plants gradually spring to life. When the occasional afternoon was pierced by a parching sun, she would hook up this lengthy phosphorescent hose and we doused her flowers and fruit trees. Afterwards, the sprinkler was attached so we could leap through the mist to cool off. Amongst the rainbow blossoms and the sweet serenade of songbirds, we quickly developed an appreciation for the beauty and fascinating wonders of nature.

Granny had a benevolent heart and for our efforts she rewarded us with some change to spend at the local candy store. These decadent treats, however, were no match for her scrumptious, wholesome meals. She pacified our bellies with her savory salads, hearty stews and sautéed salmon purchased fresh from the local fish market. Granny was getting on in years, but she exerted herself just to please us. As the summer holidays wound down, we knew the frequent visits would soon be ending, and like autumn leaves shriveling up and falling away, we sank back down to earth.

With each subsequent year at school, the fun diminished and studies took on a more serious tone. We were confronted with a new discipline called homework. I toiled as tediously as a Turkish weaver, however, and achieved excellent grades. Everyone slowly became more selective in what subjects they preferred and this seemed to have some bearing on one's future. Even our companions were chosen on the basis of some subtle distinction.

My best friend was a guy named Kenny. He was in the same classroom and much taller than I was. His long hair and baggy jeans epitomized his struggle with convention. What I liked about Kenny was his hilarious laugh. He was a born prankster and got his jollies playing tricks on many of the students. Perhaps his God-given mission was not to outdo others but to remind them how life is ever unpredictable. One time he snuck into school early and switched the signs on the bathroom doors—so none of the pupils were quite sure where to go or who to go with. Everyone ran around in a panic, but Kenny sat back as calm as a sly cat.

Steveston was on an island below sea level, so dikes had been built around the whole perimeter. There were also numerous ditches constructed alongside many of the homes to contain the heavy rains that sometimes poured down for days on end. Some of them were so wide one could paddle a canoe for miles on end. The ditch that ran adjacent to the lane beside our house was narrow with tangled brambles and overgrown, thick grasses along its banks. Kenny used to joke about the evil Slime Creature lurking in its murky depths, but catching one of the multitudes of frogs who made their habitat there was a pursuit we couldn't resist.

"Hey, Vincent, why don't we go out and see if we can nab a few frogs. I heard a really big croaker early on."

"Sure, but my frog-catcher is broken," I replied. We used to make handy frog-catchers by nailing an empty can to the end of a long stick. They weren't as efficient as a quick and agile hand, but they prevented us from constantly bending over and getting our hands filthy.

"Hey, don't worry," Kenny assured. "When we find one, I'll hold down your legs so you can lean out over the edge and grab it."

It seemed a precarious proposition at the time, but I was overly enthusiastic and equally gullible. As circumstance would have it, we spotted a plump bullfrog lounging lazily in the sun about a foot from the steep embankment. I silently shuffled into position while Kenny secured my ankles. My outstretched arm was strategically set to snatch up the critter when all of a sudden Kenny cried out, "Slime Creature, Slime Creature!"

I squiggled and frantically kicked my legs and sure enough Kenny lost his grip. Falling head first into the dreaded black scum was at the top of my list of worst possible tragedies and I skedaddled out of there with rocket ship speed that had us both rolling with laughter and amazement. It may have merely been an accident, but the experience taught me to always trust my better judgment.

Each distinct season rolled past, and in accordance, the nature of our activities followed a similar pattern. Chilly winter winds seemed to blow the sun away and the early evening darkness coerced us indoors. Like the many creatures outside, most of us hibernated in the warm burrow of our bedrooms. Apart from school days and the odd weekend, Kenny and I seldom saw one another. I enjoyed being stranded on my own island, quietly captivated with Tinker Toys or model airplanes. Likewise, my sister found stimulation with her ever expanding doll's house. Willow had a knack for inventing ingenious props to furnish each room, as if they provided real living environments for some miniature family. It was no surprise when, years later, she took courses and established a career as an accomplished interior decorator.

Sundays were family time, and we spent countless rainy afternoons conjugated in the kitchen. Like Granny, Mom used to pamper us with her cooking, although the meals were fairly basic—meat and potatoes or fish, rice and vegetables. The delicious desserts she often prepared, however, reflected only a morsel of her sweet and selfless love. Dad, Willow and I would tackle a jigsaw puzzle while she cheerfully sang in the background.

"*Que sera, sera*. Whatever will be, will be. The future's not ours to see. *Que sera, sera*."

"What should I be when I grow up?" I asked her.

And she would reply, "Always be a kind soul and life will be kind to you. Sing when there's sunshine and sing when there's rain. If you look beyond the clouds there is always a brighter life."

Over the years, puzzles of simple pictures evolved into intricate images consisting of thousands of pieces that challenged us all. With the outlandish number of fragments scattered about the kitchen table, the task of completing the puzzle seemed hopeless, but as a team we persevered and made the picture whole again. We put life back together and admired it for what it was. It was one of those magical occasions that seemed to cement the important bond between us, a bond that would prove invaluable at some point in the future.

We hardly ever went out to eat because a good portion of our food came directly to our door. Visits from the milk man, bread man, egg man and produce man were a weekly occurrence. Tommy, the produce man, was a robust, happy-go-lucky Hawaiian who drove an indigo-paneled truck that was stocked to the ceiling with the freshest fruits and vegetables. His bubbly personality was addicting and we truly appreciated it when he succumbed to our pleas to ride in the back while he called on customers in the neighborhood. He'd be humming along to tunes on the radio while we imbibed the ripe green essences floating around us.

The various provisions from these couriers all made their way to the dining room where we gathered for the daily ritual of supper. Like every chore Mom exhausted herself in perfecting, she always strived to present the meal in respectable fashion—the dishes and cutlery were displayed in an orderly manner, as if a special guest was coming. Supper was not something we rushed through, but a time to partake in the highlights of the day and reflect on the blessings of our pleasant life.

But family life wasn't always so endearing. There were moments when kids and adults just didn't see eye to eye. Like the mornings when we ranted over making the bed because it was obvious the blankets would get messed up again later that night. Like the times homework took precedent over our favorite TV show. Or the times we were forced to consume certain foods that for some strange reason made us gag. My pet peeve was canned peas and Pork n' Beans. Such mushy substances would coagulate into a formidable cold mass on my dinner plate and I could only glare back at them as the dry lump in my throat hung around like some hangman's noose. If I didn't eat them, I wouldn't get dessert and that was that.

Who knows what triggered various actions of irrational behavior, but every friend I knew was guilty of something, and we loved complaining to one another behind our parents' backs. Dad was the boss of the family empire, and in those days it was common to incorporate a leather belt to administer punishment or to simply instill fear. He used to hang the threatening black strap from a hook in the hallway closet. I seldom received a licking, but when I did, it was usually for some act committed without ever knowing what compelled me to do so or that there would be consequences for my actions. Once, at the curious age of eight, I pilfered all the cherries from our neighbor's fruit tree. There were only a few dozen in total but it was the first year the young sapling bore any fruit and the neighbor was furious. The pink welts of discipline I received left a crack between me and my dad, but a couple of days later his playful hugs and the surprise treat of an ice cream cone patched up any lingering resentment. I understood that my father's intentions were meant for my own good.

In the turmoil of adolescence, life was considerably different. Perhaps raging hormones should have shouldered some of the blame for the crazy behavior we sometimes exhibited, but more than likely it was a sign of the times. The sixties summoned a wave of social unrest and the hippie movement was intimidating to the older generations. Kenny's fashion statement no longer seemed extreme, but became the norm. My sideburns and unruly hair rendered a completely new look—and the bell-bottoms and rainbow beads didn't make things any better. Dad insisted the whole world was literally going to pot and we had our share of differing opinions. Youth's rebellious quest for freedom tore at the heartstrings of most families, creating a crevice too wide to be ignored or simply forgotten. The protests against war, politics and social injustice slowly segregated those homespun values most dear to us. For better or worse, the times were changing, and an uneasy lamentation permeated my existence. In many parts of the continent, students participated in riots, but most of my acquaintances found solace in some peaceful love-in. I preferred, instead, to contemplate the good old days playing under Granny's giant tree—but the innocent games were gone, and the warm beam of love and lush golden apples seemed a distant dream.

Perplexities Of Modern Life

Change is inevitable and we must embrace it.

Igh school graduation came too soon, but we all cel-
ebrated with the accompanying array of ceremonies,
yearbook signings and farewell parties. Most of the familiar
faces we had come to recognize or befriend would disappear
down their own path of discovery, never to be seen again. I
spent the summer working in the parks and witnessed the next
wave of young children bringing excitement and laughter to
the same spaces we once animated. The chestnut and maple
trees had grown and I was now mowing the lawns and tend-
ing the gardens and shrubbery in the manicured playgrounds
we always took for granted. Many of the graduates I knew
accepted work in town, some apprenticed for trades and a
handful heeded the call of higher learning. I was in the latter
category and thought I had made the wiser choice, but college
life was mesmerizing.

Nothing could have prepared me for the circus of open-
ing day registration or the following discipline of digesting fat
textbooks, staying awake during stale lecture seminars and
completing term papers. My head was constantly spinning,
like leaves kidnapped by the autumn breeze and tossed in a
whirlwind. In my endeavor to earn a degree in journalism, I
spent untold hours conducting research in the campus library.
Like most of the buildings, it was a prominent classical structure fashioned from heavy chiseled stone, as if to remind each
student the seriousness of their mission. My friend Kenny
only lasted three months. He was caught red-handed trying to
interchange the numbers on the doors identifying a series of
seminar rooms. The dean wouldn't have anything to do with

Kenny's cantankerous antics and expelled him immediately.

The extent of the campus was vast and I was only one of hoards of strangers rushing to and fro to get to class on time—twenty thousand shadows chasing some evasive, seemingly important knowledge that would deliver us from ignorance and prepare us with keys to new doors of golden opportunity. Eventually, I befriended a hodgepodge of delightful characters, students from different cultural backgrounds who imparted a diversity of intriguing customs and love for styles of music and cuisine with which I was unfamiliar. For the first time, my bland palate was awakened with the alluring spices and aromas of India and the Middle East, the ginger and jasmine of the Orient and the feta-filled salads of the Mediterranean infused with extra virgin olive oil. My concept of becoming educated in the ways of the world was changing. I persevered for four demanding years and, soon after, secured my first employment—as a janitor.

Thank God, Kenny's laughter was contagious. When I most needed it, his loyalty shined through and he quickly elevated my spirit. He wasn't in any better position than I was, but still approached each day as a comical adventure. Cleaning out the bathrooms in the bowels of a building can be a humbling experience. Kenny insisted I was not merely a janitor but a custodial engineer and that I should accomplish my task with pride. One soon learns to appreciate the role of every human being in life and the circumstances that place them where they are. I developed the finesse of polishing floors and cleaning windows with a sheen that would have made Felix Unger proud. My degree gathered dust in the bottom drawer of a desk but I knew my situation was temporary. Renting a dilapidated apartment in the city of Vancouver provided closer proximity to work and accessibility to the type of employment I was seeking. Opportunities were scarce, however, and

I was turned down repeatedly. Some days I drove out to the north shore to dissolve my thoughts along the wooded trails or up the winding path to some mountain summit, but when I returned I still had to face the problem at hand. Patience became a burdening exercise. The recollection of my mom's advice to look beyond the clouds resonated in my sparsely furnished suite, but as the months shot by, I was overcome with episodes of remorse.

Friends who assisted on fishing vessels back home or developed a trade were light years ahead of me. With their income, some purchased their own homes and many accumulated new cars or an assortment of popular appliances, while I was still paying off the loan for my tuition. I obtained a degree and deserved a break, I thought. It was easy to place the blame on the callousness of society, but it only fueled my bitterness. Trapped in disillusion, I became depressed and gradually withdrew from the world. I ceased preparing refreshing, wholesome meals and substituted cheap fare from nearby fast food joints. My appetite waned and I now indulged in alcohol, never realizing how the combined stress of poor lifestyle habits depleted my energy and triggered bouts of illness. There were nights filled with sleepless anxiety or passing daydreams that rose up and lulled my loneliness, only to disappear into the distance with disinterest. I was lost down some gloomy road and there was no light to see a way out. It was then, when the phone shrieked like a siren, that I received some shocking news that broke the spell I was encased in. It seems the Big Bad Wolf was back, but it had a new name called Cancer, and Granny was its latest victim.

"What am I...are we going to...can we do, Vincent?" Mom was crying and her words were jumbled with emotion. I could tell by the gravity of her voice how serious it was and tried to console her.

"Poor old Granny, she just doesn't deserve this," I moaned. "But what does it mean? What do the doctors say?"

Mom collected herself before responding. "The cancer is in the colon, but it has already spread. She doesn't have a very good chance."

"Modern medicine must have something...doesn't it? What does Dad have to say?" I inquired.

"I've never seen him act so helpless. He mostly sits around in silence, dumbfounded."

While Mom embraced life through the open channels of her heart, Dad functioned primarily from the rational structure of his mind. This was hard for him. He initially interrogated the head physician to no end, but didn't have any context on the subject of cancer to draw from. Like most people, we all just sat back and followed whatever protocol the doctor prescribed.

Granny underwent chemotherapy and rigorous radiation treatments and her condition deteriorated rapidly. Within a few months, she withered away to a pale skeleton before our very eyes. She detested the sterile shell of a room at the hospital and spent most of her final weeks at home, surrounded by her plants and the comfort of family members and close friends. The morphine injections that were given to disguise the severe pain made her hallucinate. It was time for us to say farewell to a sweet soul who no longer knew who she was.

"Nothing like the death of someone near to you to make you re-evaluate your life," my sister mumbled. Willow was living on the East Coast now and had flown back for the funeral. I wasn't sure if the comment was directed at me or not, but she was dead on.

"Yes, I've been soaking in my own self-pity and it just doesn't seem justified, especially when so many people are worse off," I replied. "Granny must have been in a ton of pain these past few years but she never complained. She kept her misery to herself, yet found the inner strength and courage to enrich the lives of so many others."

"Oh Vincent! My remark wasn't aimed at you. I was implying how modern life in general is just getting so complex. So many of us are running around like chickens with their heads cut off, riding the latest wave or chasing the newest trend. We move to wherever the next job opportunity takes us. It's like playing follow the leader—but we don't truly know who the leader is or if their promise will benefit us or mainly benefit them."

"I see what you mean, Willow. We don't even live in the same town we grew up in. Just the distance makes it harder to confide in long-time friends. There are no family dinners to share the events of the day and the dreamy life of childhood and hippies are a thing of the past. But I'm reluctant to jump on the Yuppie bandwagon in an attempt to keep pace with the expanding corporate world and the dawning of this so-called Information Era."

"I guess we just have to trust in God's plan, Vincent. Life will probably never be the same. In fact it might keep moving forward, faster and faster and faster. Perhaps this is what ate away at Granny—her children moved away, then her grandchildren, then some of her kind neighbors, until the loving life that nurtured her soul was lured away, leaving a vacant mansion of memories and ghosts."

By the time I arrived back home from the funeral I was determined. I now realized there was no free ticket, no magic carpet, or no easy path to a long and peaceful life. When you least expected it, some mysterious menace would breathe down your neck or block the way, prompting your fortitude or challenging your preconceptions and your faith. I couldn't comprehend how a loving God could inflict Granny, or for that matter any sincere soul, with a wrath the likes of cancer.

Why weren't their prayers answered? Was there no cure in sight? If God and his army of angels were alive, where was their miracle?

Over the next few months, I spent as much time as possible immersed in research at the downtown library. I wanted to learn more about this deadly disease—what caused it, how was it treated and why were the results so dismal? It was refreshing to get out in public again and the volume of texts I perused was like a sparkplug recharging my mind. I drafted my findings into a passionate article and sent it off to a handful of newspapers and magazines. Three weeks later it appeared in a community paper:

THE DARKEST HOUR
by Vincent Young

I cannot sleep tonight. These eyes keep staring back at me and they are not my own. They are eyes transfixed in terror. They are silent, yet I sense their deafening scream. The eyes belong to a special friend and their final hour has come. Every dream they've lived for, every thought they've shared, and every heart they've touched or has touched them, are precious experiences all dissolving away. My special friend has succumbed to this fierce struggle with cancer and for some time now I have been at a loss to help them.

Seven years ago President Nixon declared war on cancer. Since that time over three million Americans have lost their lives to this fatal disease—fifty times the number of casualties suffered during the sixteen year war in Viet Nam. Their battle was as heroic as any soldier, yet they passed away in silence to an enemy that still rages on. There is no grand memorial that bears their name, no gun salute and no mass rioting against the machinery that allows it to persist on homeland soil. In Canada this travesty is equally severe, with an estimated one-third of the population becoming afflicted with some form of cancer in their lifetime. We can fly to the moon, but we cannot stop this alien who invades our very own home.

Cancer is a chronic degenerative condition characterized by the uncontrolled growth and spread of abnormal cells. The human body is composed of some ten trillion cells each carrying out their unique biological functions. These cells are constantly replicating to replace those that are dying off. In the case of cancer cells, the controlled manner with which they multiply becomes quite abnormal. It is believed a variety of toxic agents contribute to these rebel cells reproducing at will, cloning independent colonies that infiltrate the surrounding tissue. These cell mutations may result from internal factors such as hormones, metabolic imbalances and weak immune response, or from an accumulation of external factors such as tobacco, radiation, chemical pollutants and food preservatives.

A good portion of the patients who have cancer will receive some type of radiation therapy, usually in combination with other treatments. Radiation therapy incorporates streams of x-ray waves or energy particles to destroy cancer cells or damage their DNA and prevent them from continuing to multiply. The radiation beams can be targeted directly to the area being treated, but there is often damage to the surrounding healthy tissue. Side effects can include dry or itchy skin, redness, scaring, dry mouth, hair loss or fatigue.

Apart from surgery, the other common form of

treatment involves the use of chemical drugs or chemotherapy. In chemotherapy a variety of drug types
and administration modules are utilized to destroy the
cancer cells. These chemicals can be extremely harsh
and many people fear the side effects associated with
their application—nausea, vomiting, fever, chills, tired-
ness, loss of appetite, hair loss, skin rashes, lower blood
count and muscle pain. Chemotherapy is known as a
systemic treatment, which means that it travels through
your entire body, unlike surgery or radiation which
concentrates on one specific area. Chemotherapy may
cause the tumor to shrink or slow down its growth and
is often applied when it is believed the cancer cells have
spread to other areas of the body. As some cancer cells
undergo genetic changes that allow them to produce
enzymes that override a drug's usefulness, combinations of drugs are often prescribed. Further drugs are
often recommended just to deal with the side effects
from the different treatments.

It just doesn't make any sense. By the time a tumor
develops and has taken a foothold, the body has consistently been compromised with a plethora of toxins and
stress. By the time a victim is imprisoned in so much
pain and exhaustion and they reach out in desperation to their physician, their digestion and immune
system have already faltered. It is then that they are
injected with chemicals so lethal some could burn a
hole through the surface of a floor if accidentally spilled
upon it. Yet only the mighty medical association has
been sanctioned with the power to dictate the designs
of our treatment. And just like the mass extermination
of Jews in the Second World War, or the annihilation
of the citizens of Hiroshima and Nagasaki with atomic

bombs, these modern acts against humanity seem so horrendous.

Although a seemingly insurmountable institution administers our fate, it is we who are to blame. It is the individual who allows their emotions to fester uncontrolled like a plague inside their mind and body. It is the individual who habitually stuffs their living temple with plate after plate of depleted food. It is the individual who incessantly smokes or drinks until they plunge into a stupor, despite the toll it takes on themselves or their family. And it is the spoiled and decadent culture we so often adhere to that provides a breeding ground for our selfish and destructive behavior. We can only pray for the strength to change.

Almost every great challenge in life makes us stronger. As mankind delves deeper into the soul of this problem, the solutions will be there, and only those solutions that are selfless and based on the betterment of mankind will provide the promising results we seek. When we rise up beyond our fear, we will be liberated with infinite possibilities.

The newspaper printed two successive articles I submitted on cancer and they helped launch my career as a journalist. My bolstered résumé secured a series of jobs with various publications and before too long I was traveling throughout the country to investigate the latest story. I was no longer a couch potato waiting for a lucky break, but a competitor racing to keep up with the demands of my profession. Over the next twenty-five years, I was part of the motion that made the world whiz by. I lived in five different cities and only visited my parents at Christmas or while on vacation. Regular phone calls kept me in touch with Mom, but communication with

Dad became increasingly distant. Traffic jams, airport terminals and Starbucks, where I refueled my energy with adrenal-charging caffeine, became common new playgrounds I reluctantly adjusted to. My sister was right—human activity on much of the planet was speeding up. The advent of fax machines and cell phones, coupled with a relentless fixation on advancing computer technology, made sure of that. Keeping pace with the latest innovations was both distracting and challenging. I often wondered if there was some wisdom behind it all.

Today I sit exhausted on the balcony of my hi-rise apartment. It is early summer and I take a moment to enjoy the companionship of the sun and the potted flowers I have arranged around me. Pink fuchsia paired with blue lobelia dangle in baskets from the beam above. They are peaceful, yet I sometimes gaze beyond them at the bustling streets below. It is another strange city and the same questions still haunt me. Will mankind's assumed mastery of science and technology deliver us or eventually destroy us? Will genetic manipulation or exploring the microscopic dimensions of quantum energy bring us healing or hindrance? The Internet has given us instant access to a universe of information, but are we any more enlightened? And like myself, have we grown out of touch with the magical rhythms of nature and will we ever find our way back home?

A Family In Crisis

In our deepest tragedy lies our highest realization.

How God's children have scattered like seeds in the wind. I was feeling a little out of touch with my roots and decided to take a break and head back home. My parents were still living in the same old rambler I grew up in, except it was now enshrouded by towering oaks and bushes, as if keeping pace with the burgeoning world. The scene always brought back fond memories and it was a pleasure to immerse myself again with familiar company. My presence put a sparkle in the eyes of my mother, and communicating with Dad on the recent articles I had written was rewarding. He didn't always agree with my viewpoint but dished out more compliments than advice.

"I must say I'm proud of you son. You do a remarkable job of putting together a compelling piece and encouraging people to see the broader aspects of each issue you present."

"My goal has always been to stir the consciousness," I asserted. "Even if it awakens the attitude or opens the mind of a few searching souls, it is worth the effort. So many people return home exhausted at the end of their work day and vegetate by reading the newspaper or flipping through channels on their TV sets. I once did a project on television and discovered that two-thirds of the shows airing most nights deal with conflict, competition or manipulation. This type of input only floods the mind with negative thoughts."

"I fully agree," Dad responded. "That's why I've taken up a few new hobbies since my retirement." Sitting at a desk for thirty years with a white-collar job had tempered my dad's ambitious footsteps, but he still exhibited an intrinsic motive to accomplish things. Jude had already shown me the patio he had constructed in the back of the house and the renovations he had completed in the basement and master bathroom. However, his eagerness was more obvious when he brought out all the charts he had compiled on the various species of feathered friends he had witnessed since taking up bird watching. Dad had logs on everything from tiny hummingbirds to the great horned owl with its impressive wingspan. He knew the different markings that identified a specific bird and was even learning some of their behavior patterns and distinctive songs.

"I'm glad to see you've found a way to keep busy, Dad. After committing so many years to a rigid schedule of work hours it must be challenging. So what do you do to keep yourself busy, Mom?"

"Sometimes I putter in the garden, but mostly I spend a lot of time reading books."

"What kinds of books do you like the best?" I inquired.

"Mostly romantic novels or epic adventures set in some timeless, exotic location. I think I've read over three hundred books in the last few years and I'm getting bored with them. It was much more fulfilling taking care of you all, but I hardly see you or Willow anymore."

Mom had always been the inspiration and guiding light of the family and it was hard to see her changed condition. My pursuit in uplifting her spirit involved coaxing her out of the house and disrupting her routine. A trip to Stanley Park to visit the zoo and indulge in a family picnic seemed to do the trick, but soon afterwards Mom reverted to her former state. It was as if her energy was constantly zapped away and I noticed the way she trudged through her daily chores and struggled to prepare one of her signature dinners. Even her appetite had stagnated and she appeared to have lost some weight. Mom didn't want to set off any alarms, but did confess that she had been experiencing some discomfort in one of her breasts. Dad and I discussed it and convinced her to have a checkup with the doctor. Since our long-time family physician had recently passed away, Mom was assigned a new replacement who reviewed her prior medical history, conducted a thorough physical examination and took some blood tests. The doctor didn't divulge much, but I had my doubts and suspected something serious was about to unfold. My worst fears were confirmed when he called Mom back and advised her to undergo a mammogram.

The mood in the car was a little somber the day we drove to the cancer clinic for Mom's test. It was a modern complex that housed a diverse group of medical specialists and sophisticated diagnostic and treatment services. Being in that kind of environment again was like unscrewing the lid off a jar of disturbing memories.

It's strange how worrying can get the best of us. Dad and I hadn't eaten all day and we eventually started pacing the foyer together. I needed to focus so I grabbed a couple of the informational brochures on the counter and commenced leafing through them. They indicated that breast cancer is the most frequently diagnosed cancer in women and that it ranked second among female mortalities in this category. It was reassuring to read that death rates from this disease had been recently declining due to a combination of early detection and improvements in treatment.

"Hasn't Mom ever had a mammogram before?" I asked Dad. "It says that precancerous changes can occur years before they evolve into invasive carcinoma and that regular testing is recommended."

"Maybe years back son, but until recently she's always been so chipper and positive about life. I can't ever recall her complaining about her health."

"It says here that the risk of breast cancer is increased by inherited genetic mutations in certain genes. Has anyone in her family history suffered from this type of cancer?" I prodded.

"Her sister died from complications due to breast cancer, but let's not get ahead of ourselves son. We don't even know the results of her test yet."

"Yes, I guess it's best if we remain positive—no matter what the verdict we need to give Mom all the support in the world."

At times like this, the hands of a clock move painfully slow and one needs to cultivate the virtue of patience. Dad and I remained restless, so for the next couple of days we wiled away the hours playing cribbage. The results finally came back and the mammography detected the presence of a suspicious lump or lesion. I sensed we were about to embark on a long and challenging journey.

The family doctor subsequently set up an appointment with an oncologist he knew at the clinic. We were all filled with a nervous apprehension, but our tensions dispersed the moment we met the specialist. He was a congenial fellow with an infectious laugh that immediately made us all feel comfortable. The soft-spoken, gentle giant introduced himself as Dr. Shepherd and invited us back to his office. Although he appeared much younger than any of us, the diplomas mounted on the wall behind him solicited our respect. The framed portraits of his wife and children that stood before the tidy stacks of paperwork on his desk reminded us he was simply a human being performing the duties of his chosen profession. After some preliminary questions, he described the concept and various functions of the center. It was pretty obvious the technology surrounding cancer had evolved substantially since the days of Granny's ordeal. Mom remained in his office while Dad and I were instructed to wait in the lobby. It was weird watching the procession of patients coming and going, their composed faces offering little clue as to the nature of their problem. Some might have been there merely for a checkup, and some might have been clinging onto their existence by the thin thread of a lifeline.

When Mom reappeared, she explained that Dr. Shepherd recommended further tests to determine the status of the lump. She consented to an ultrasound, an imaging technique in which high-frequency sound waves are bounced off body tissues or internal organs. The echoes from these sound waves produce a picture called a sonogram. Ultrasound imaging of Mom's breast could help ascertain the size of the lesion, as well as distinguish whether it was a solid tumor or a fluid-filled cyst. Due to their busy staff schedule, we were informed the ultrasound couldn't be performed until next week. Fortunately, we received a phone call from the clinic the following morning. A patient had cancelled her appointment so they were able to squeeze Mom in that afternoon.

An unexpected rainstorm viciously pelted the Fraser Valley. Dad and I could only sit in the shelter of the waiting room and silently pray. Before too long, Dr. Shepherd came out all calm and collected and we were all over him like eager puppies fraternizing with a customer at a pet store. He stated that the results would be available in a few days and we should wait for his call. When we drove Mom back home, she too showed no signs of anxiety and softly sang her favorite song by Doris Day.

For the first time, I suddenly realized my parents weren't getting any younger, and that one day I would have to confront the reality of them dying. No matter how simple or how severe, the onslaught of symptoms that arise with aging often provoke our worst suspicions. Death was a mystery I hadn't prepared for. I hand no inkling of how I would react to it and how it might affect me emotionally. It seems I had some homework to do.

The local bookstore had a small section dealing with the predicament of dying and I curiously scanned through them the following afternoon. Many of the authors offered sensitive insights and encouraging advice on the subject. I jotted down some ideas of what I perceived was a synthesis of their thoughts:

The fear of death is universal and is no less traumatic today than it has been throughout the course of civilization, but how each of us deals with the experience can be substantially different. Coping with this inevitable and mysterious event springs to the surface a gamut of human emotions ranging from fear and guilt to anger and anguish. These emotions are not only agitated in the critically ill or dying, but in the immediate circle of family and friends as well. There is often a tendency to repress one's anxiety and retreat into a lonely silence, yet openly confronting death presents a golden opportunity for reconciliation and healing. It is not a time to accuse God or society of being unjust, nor a time to place blame upon ourselves or any acquaintance whose actions may have seemed to tarnish our world with conflict. The circumstances that led up to this moment must be forgiven to achieve inner peace. Standing on the doorstep of the unknown, we can witness our life and all its complexity slipping away, or we can peer deep into the preciousness of our existence and see the simple beauty of our journey. There is always hope for what lies beyond. There is always hope for those we leave behind. We are so fragile, yet when we hover in humbleness at the edge of our vulnerability, our spirit is strengthened and restored. Open communication and communion on the part of the patient, family and doctor can be a resurrecting force. Any event that stirs us to reach out in compassion, or inspires us to re-establish our values and the attitude with which we approach life, can only be a blessing. It is never too late for the rejuvenating power of love to perform its miracle.

When the results of the ultrasound finally came back and we learned Mom did have a solid tumor, we were temporarily infused with shock. The news hit Dad hard, but thanks to my recent research I encouraged everyone to stay calm and approach the situation rationally. When I confronted Willow with the news, she broke down crying and decided to fly out the following day. She had a ten year old son now, and since he was out of school for the summer, he accompanied her on the trip out west. Calin was a sweet little boy with an inquisitive mind that assured the communication in the household would stay afloat.

"What's wrong with Granny?" he inquired. "Is she going to be okay?"

"Don't worry, Calin," Willow assured. "Mom might have a serious illness, but we'll all work together to try and overcome it."

"Is it cancer?" Calin blurted out. "My best friend's mom had cancer and she lost all her hair."

"Her hair didn't fall out because of the cancer, Calin, but because of the treatment." I explained how chemotherapy is designed to kill the most active cells in the body first, which are primarily those associated with the tumor, but hair follicles, gastrointestinal and bone marrow cells are also affected. We all spent endless hours discussing Mom's condition, even though further tests still had to be conducted to see if the tumor was malignant or had metastasized. During one of these sessions I came up with an idea.

"Remember when we used to sit around the kitchen table and construct these crazy jigsaw puzzles? I would gather all the people images, Willow would piece together the buildings and Dad would tackle the surrounding landscape. After we completed our own section, we'd simply set them in place and the only thing left was to complete the sky. Once we established this pattern of pursuit, the most thwarting puzzles were no longer a predicament."

"What are you driving at?" Dad asked curiously.

"Well, why don't we focus on solving the puzzle called cancer in the same way? I was thinking Willow could explore traditional therapies and the benefits of incorporating a healthy diet."

"What about me?" Dad interjected. "I'm not sure if I believe in all that stuff. Are you willing to risk your Mom's fate on some unproven procedure?"

"Right now, no one knows the extent of the problem or has the perfect answer, but at least if we compile as much information as we can and explore all the options, perhaps the most sensible solution will be evident. Why should we blindly follow the advice of any doctor or oncologist, Dad? Why don't you take a hard look at conventional treatment methods? Nowadays, they have all kinds of targeted designer drugs and sophisticated computer technology that makes the diagnosis and follow-up procedures so much more precise."

"What are you going to investigate, Vincent?"

"I'll look into integrative cancer centers and the balancing effects of healing energy work. I'll try and locate and inter-view surviving cancer patients. I'll talk to the staff at health food stores about effective herbal remedies and nutritional supplements. Heck, I'll read as many books on the subject as I can find."

"I love the idea!" Willow remarked with new optimism. "Instead of waiting in fear, at least we'll keep ourselves busy, and who knows what we might discover and come to learn in the process."

"You all give me so much hope," Mom uttered. "It's just so nice to see the whole family together again." Mom had been sitting quietly to the side and in our strategic discussion we temporarily forgot she was still in the room. "With your devoted support and God's grace, I have faith that the right path to take will become clear. Everything happens for various reasons, and as we come to understand those reasons, I believe our lives will become better for it."

Conventional Complications

The normal way we do things is not normal.

During the time lapse of waiting around for other appointments and further test results, Willow, Dad and I busied ourselves researching our respective parts of the cancer puzzle. The resources available at the library and on the Internet proved promising. We sat down one evening and intently listened to Dad's findings:

"Breast cancer is one of the most challenging experiences a woman will confront in her lifetime," he explained. "The United States, for instance, has one of the highest breast cancer rates in the world and each year approximately 180,000 women are diagnosed with this disease. Thank God the five-year survival rate has recently improved and the majority of candidates survive well beyond that duration if they commit themselves to making informed decisions and following through with an effective treatment program. The size of the tumor, the stage of the cancer and the risks factors involved should all be carefully weighed before making a preferred choice."

"This is probably going to involve a lot of time and cooperation with a variety of caregivers," I stipulated. "We might as well get used to it and abide by proceeding one step at a time."

"We did have a very encouraging discussion with Dr. Shepherd again this morning. The primary focus of his practice is actually on breast cancer. The more your mother and I get to know him, the more we appreciate his knowledge on the subject and the time he takes to thoroughly explain things. He seems quite sincere and compassionate and we're glad to have chosen his services to manage her treatment. He even supports the investigation you are both conducting on complementary therapeutic options and emphasized the value of working as a unified team and pooling all of our resources together to achieve the best results."

"Did Dr. Shepherd elaborate any further on the results of the ultrasound?" I asked.

"When Dr. Shepherd conferred with the radiologist, he indicated the size of the tumor to be approximately two centimeters in width. A tumor that size might be somewhat advanced, but no one really knows how fast growing or aggressive it is. To put things in perspective, he explained that a lump usually appears after one abnormal cell divides or doubles at least thirty times. Depending on the background and state of the person, this doubling speed can take anywhere from a few months to even years before a tumor can be detected. At that point, the tumor could consist of over a billion cells."

"Gee whiz!" Willow bellowed. "It makes you wonder how long the damn thing has been festering away inside Mom."

Willow's freckles looked like they were springing up in their own cellular protest. I managed to remain composed and asked Dad about any other information he had discovered.

"The cloud surrounding cancer is quite complicated and difficult to master," Dad said. "At the library I did find a report specifying that the American Joint Committee on Cancer classified cancers according to the TNM system and most medical facilities honored it. This system defines the various stages of cancer according to specific combinations of three distinct groupings, but the details of each stage vary depending on the size of the tumor and the extent to which it has spread."

"So what are these three groupings, Dad?"

Dad slowly read from the basic chart he had copied:

"T indicates the size of the primary tumor and if it has started invading nearby body tissues.

N refers to whether any lymph nodes have been infiltrated from the primary tumor and how large any related metastases might be.

M denotes if the cancer has spread to other organs and to what degree the metastasis has occurred."

"As a cancer progresses," he continued, "it undergoes numerous changes and a complex array of symptoms are produced. Cancer cells are like parasites and they can eventually develop their own network of blood vessels that suck away the nourishment from a person's main blood supply. Wherever an aggressive tumor takes root, it starts to secrete enzymes that interact with the surrounding tissue, altering molecules and paving the way for its destructive and unpredictable course."

"It seems there are so many factors involved—it's almost impossible to pinpoint what precipitates cancer, where it will migrate to and what degree of damage it is capable of inflicting," I concluded

"That's the reason a biopsy is so commonly performed," Dad said.

"What is a biopy?" Calin asked. Calin was busy painting with watercolors on the table and we were all surprised he was even listening to our discussion. I suddenly realized he was no less innocent to the information than all of us were.

"A biopsy," Dad corrected, "is when they remove a sampling of tissue from a suspicious lump or tumor and examine it under a microscope. Dr. Shepherd recommended a biopsy to help decipher the nature of the tumor. If the tumor is benign, or non-malignant, it is not life-threatening and can simply be surgically removed. But if it is malignant, there is the serious threat that the cancer cells could be invasive and spread to other parts of the body."

"So that seems like the next course of action?" Willow asked.

"Yes, it seems the sensible thing to do at this point and we trust the advice of the doctor."

"Can't that be kind of painful?"

"There could be some discomfort and a little scarring, but it all depends on the type of biopsy performed and the amount of tissue that is removed. Dr. Shepherd informed us of a less invasive technique known as fine-needle aspiration. They just inject a needle to obtain a tissue sample or a small quantity of fluid from the tumor, and the whole procedure can be performed in the doctor's office under local anesthesia. There is less risk involved than in a surgical biopsy, where complications such as excessive bleeding or infection may occur. Of course, the more tissue they extract, the more a pathologist has to work with and examine under a microscope."

"So you agreed on the needle biopsy?" I asked.

"That's right. I'll be taking your mother back in three days to have this done. We hope it will provide a clue in determining the stage and invasive nature of the tumor."

"What does the stage of the tumor indicate?"

"Breast cancer is classified into one of five different stages— anywhere from 0 to 4. Based on the size of Mom's lump, it has most likely progressed to a Stage 1 or 2. Stage 1 tumors are no greater than two centimeters in diameter, the lymph nodes are not involved and there is no spread of the cancer at this early stage. In Stage 2 the size of the tumor is between two and five centimeters, without lymph node involvement, or involving only those lymph nodes under the armpit on the same side as the infected breast and without any evidence of distant metastasis."

"So once a professional diagnosis is made, we can all sit down and discuss a common sense strategy regarding the treatment?"

"Yes, and it could get complicated. Just as there are different diagnostic procedures, there is a wide range of conventional treatment modalities. Each oncologist has their own unique preferences regarding patient management, although there are standard guidelines with respect to the type of surgery performed, the form of radiation delivered or the class of drugs administered as chemotherapy. There are acknowledged approaches one can follow, but there are also many new refinements and innovations in dealing with breast cancer. The recent advances in immunology, molecular biology and genetics offer even more effective and less toxic avenues of therapy. The treatment landscape is constantly changing and the options available today will probably expand a few years down the road."

"As long as we just don't stand around awestruck like we did with Granny." I had been waiting for an appropriate moment to throw in that reminder. "We need to be more proactive and not be afraid to think out of the box."

"The majority of people I come into contact with seem to spend most of their time living in a box," Willow asserted. "Perhaps it's a reflection of my career, but we primarily function in an indoor shell far removed from the natural world that God created. The home, the office, the car or the coffee shop will never compete with the dynamics of a vast canyon, a pristine forest or some simple seashore."

Willow had a knack for getting me started, so I jumped right in with my additional comments. "A few die-hards find time to squeeze in regular workouts at the gym or pop a handful of vitamins to propel them through the day, but it hardly compensates for the all too common existence lost in paperwork, newspapers or books, or sitting in front of a TV or computer screen with another microwave dinner. And when an illness eventually sets in, we often rush off to the pharmacy for a box of pills to magically vanish the symptoms of our sedentary life. There are moments I get so frustrated when I observe how this orthodox world has limited us and how off-center our modern lifestyle has become."

"You know son, sometimes we need to veer off course to find ourselves. You and Willow have had the luxury of living in so many different places and experiencing aspects of life that your mom and I never have. My philosophy and pursuits in life have become somewhat conservative and focused and there are days I regret not having wandered off the beaten path a little more, but it's who I am now and I wouldn't change it even if I could start all over again."

"I guess I shouldn't be so judgmental, Dad. Each path has its pitfalls and possibilities and everyone is striving to find meaning in their own way. I just don't want Mom to become another premature victim of the times."

"Cancer is so complex and how we address it probably reflects a great deal of how we approach life. The solutions we all seek are often mired in confusion and controversy, but we have to find and choose our own way. I'm anxious to hear what enlightening views you and Willow have recently discovered."

Traditional Healing Wisdom

The insights of the past are our guide to the future.

The next morning the sky was clear and warm sunlight shimmered on the petals of roses and other decorative blooms that surrounded the patio. We decided to enjoy breakfast outdoors in this picturesque setting and we all pitched in to prepare a simple feast of fruit salad, cheddar cheese omelets, whole grain toast and fresh-squeezed orange juice. Afterwards, Mom toured us around the garden and pointed out her favorite plants, while Calin chased a pair of butterflies and befriended a caterpillar that gradually plodded along his pant leg and arm until it made its way up to his shoulder.

"How can something so slow and fuzzy turn into an iridescent butterfly?" he inquired.

"Perhaps it's a magic that happens when the old integrates with the new." My reply was painted by the contemplation of incorporating both traditional and conventional methodology in dealing with cancer. When we sat back down again, we resumed the next segment of our discussion.

"What have you dug up regarding alternative medicine, Willow?" I asked.

"I primarily focused on the rationale behind ancient medicine and found it to be quite different from the modern approach we so readily adopt in Western culture. The development of traditional Chinese medicine, for instance, began over 3,000 years ago and was based on folk medicine rooted in classical belief systems. It embraces the philosophical concept that the human body is a small universe composed of sophisticated interconnected systems, and that these systems must be in balance to maintain the healthy function of the individual.

Observation and feedback from the patient plays a key role in the diagnosis and treatment. Herbal medicine, dietary therapy, acupuncture, massage, and exercises in breathing and movement such as qi gong and tai chi, are incorporated.

The principle of *yin* and *yang* lies at the foundation of Chinese medicine. It examines the many ways in which the fundamental balance between yin —cool, expansive and passive properties, and yang—warm, constrictive and active properties, may be undermined and how to re-establish a harmonious and rhythmic polarity between the two."

Mom and Dad were incessantly shifting in their chairs and were probably unfamiliar with some of the terms. I was impressed with how fast Willow seemed to grasp this new information and I still had a few questions of my own.

"What about the characteristics of wood and fire and water—aren't they involved as well?" I voiced.

"Yes, the five elemental energies of wood, fire, earth, metal and water also play a major role in traditional Chinese medicine. Their distinct properties have a relationship to specific organs and their vital functions, bodily fluids, mental and emotional states, as well as food and medicinal herbs. The interplay between these elemental energies provides a practical working model for understanding and treating the human body. For instance, a personality with a strong fire presence tends to overheat the inner organs and often has an overactive heart. They should avoid alcohol and stimulating yang foods, and then balance their excess fire with cooling yin foods and calming herbs associated with the water element. Basically, the tradition as a whole places a large emphasis in lifestyle management in order to prevent disease as well as recuperate from an illness."

"Even though traditional Chinese medicine is slowly gaining popularity in the west, I heard that in China and other

Asian countries it is considered an integral part of the health care system."

"It is, Vincent, and now that I comprehend it a little more, I only hope it continues to grow."

"What else have you looked into?" Mom's question held a hint of enthusiasm, even though she couldn't quite fathom the full meaning of what was being said.

Willow then explained the basic principals of Ayurvedic medicine to everyone. "Ayurveda is another alternative medical practice that is popular in India and also claims to be thousands of years old. Since the majority of India's population lives in rural areas, about two-thirds of rural dwellers still use Ayurveda and medicinal plants to meet their primary health care needs. Many of these people subsist on a minimal income, and the availability of this system of healing is more accessible and less expensive than trekking to a major hospital for treatment. The central concept of Ayurvedic medicine is the theory that sound health exists when there is a balance between three fundamental bodily substances or *doshas* called *vata, pitta* and *kapha*. The doshas regulate mind-body harmony and each patient is classified as primarily one of these three types. Vata represents the elements of air and ether, and allegedly governs all movement in the mind and body, and is necessary to mobilize the function of the nervous system. Too much vata leads to worrying, insomnia and constipation. A proper balance ensures healthy circulation, breathing and elimination of wastes. Pitta represents the elements of fire and water and allegedly governs all heat, metabolism and transformation in the mind and body. It controls how we digest food and how our sensory perceptions operate. Too much pitta energy can lead to anger, criticism and ulcerations in the body. The last one, kapha, represents the elements of water and earth and governs the material elements of our physical structure. This dosha relates to mucus, the lubrication of joints, the moisture of the skin, the healing of wounds and the general strength of the body. Too much kapha energy can lead to attachment, greed and envy and can manifest as weight gain and congestion. Apart from applying certain foods and herbs to restore balance to the body, mind and spirit, amulets or mantras are sometimes incorporated as well."

"This all sounds very interesting," Mom ventured, "but I'm not sure how it applies to my condition."

"At least we're gaining a larger perspective on health and healing," I affirmed. "We need to explore these options further, perhaps with qualified practitioners versed in these traditional approaches, but a few things seem quite clear. Unlike conventional therapy, they address the whole person and harness the energy existing in nature to assist the body in healing itself."

Willow explained that in early Western civilization cancer and other illnesses were treated with ointments, enemas, poultices, plants and even animal parts, with ritual playing an important role. Medicine and myth were closely intermingled and various deities were often associated with either disease or the healing process. "Perhaps people felt the Gods cursed them with an illness or an accident if their actions were selfish or harmful to others, but if they atoned for their behavior, they had faith the Gods would smile down upon them and deliver away their affliction."

"Didn't Hippocrates lift medicine out of the realm of superstition and equate disease as a natural process that required observation and physical therapy to treat?" I questioned.

"Yes, but in his day Greek physicians and philosophers also respected the interplay of universal elements. Earth, air, water and fire were each affiliated with the corresponding qualities of cold, dry, moist and hot. They theorized that disease developed as a result of an imbalance of these characteristics. It was also believed that four bodily fluids, or humors, governed a person's health. An imbalance of blood, phlegm, yellow bile or black bile were indications of ill health, and for centuries it was believed that cancer was caused by an excess of black bile. Of course, the exploration of anatomy during the Renaissance and, later on, the invention of the microscope and the discovery of cells introduced a whole new perspective toward the protocols of medicine. Research became invariably focused on the inner structures of the human body and the art of healing gradually became a narrow science."

"But we can't just treat the disease," I urged. "We have to resurrect our whole body, transform our thought patterns and empower our spirit with uplifting emotions."

Mom agreed and Willow and I both let out a sigh of relief. "It does make a lot of sense to me. I used to feel so positive about everything, but sometimes life gets the better of us."

Dad had been listening in silence and finally spoke out in support, "This complex world has changed drastically over the past twenty years. I believe it's gotten the best of many people. Terrorists, global warming, reality TV shows, complex computer gadgets and who knows what's coming next. We've lost touch with familiarity. Heck, I even get into a fizzle with simple technology."

"What do you mean?" we all asked in unison.

"For thirty years I used to lather my face with a brush and an inexpensive cup of Old Spice shaving soap that lasted for months. I cherished this old chrome razor that I'd slot a flat blade into and manually adjusted the setting to suit my beard. I resisted, but finally graduated to a track-two blade that was nonadjustable. Just as I was feeling comfortable, they came out with three blades, then four and now five. These new blades don't even fit the old razor, so you have to purchase a whole new set. Just the act of shaving last year cost me over three hundred dollars."

"Technology does create fierce competition, Dad, and the consumer is often the victim of exploitation, but look at the bright side—you're bald now and you no longer have to pay for haircuts!" I loved ribbing Dad sometimes and everyone had a good chuckle. The situation could have been quite solemn, but we transcended the experience with our enthusiasm, encouragement and comradeship.

After further discussion, it was decided we had enough for one day and retired indoors. Mom and I collaborated on a healthy supper of stir-fries, jasmine rice and green tea, while Dad and Willow tutored Calin on the fine art of constructing a jigsaw puzzle. To an observer, we would have appeared a normal family involved in the events of the evening, though an invisible air of kindness permeated through us all. After dinner, Dad washed the dishes and I wiped them dry. Then both of us gave the entire kitchen a thorough cleaning, which elicited some warm hugs from Mom. Together we had faith we would get through this and that the right course of action was something we all had to share.

Sometimes a serious event or illness can bring forth the brighter qualities in people. It is so easy to take others for granted, forgetting the silent struggle we often face as we journey through life. Compassion is a virtue we all need to exercise, and when we give from the heart, the barriers of communication dissolve away and the scars of personal wounds undergo the process of healing.

Gift From A Medicine Man

Life is a dream that always comes true.

Later that evening Willow and I enjoyed a quiet evening sitting outside under the summer stars. The warm night air was calm, but my mind was stirring with the latest research I had uncovered. She sensed something promising was about to burst through, but I held my silence until all of us met again in the morning. I slept little, engulfed in thoughts of whether the news I was about to share would be the breakthrough we were seeking.

Everyone arose bright and early at dawn, uplifted with the celestial gift of a coral-streaked horizon. Mom steeped a pot of tea that we all savored out on the patio. We calmly watched the rising sun melt away the dew drops and awaken the sweet peas and snapdragons.

"So what did you find out, Vincent?" Willow asked curiously.

"I went around to a half dozen health food stores and asked what remedies might be beneficial for cancer."

"And what did they suggest?"

"Some of the staff recommended mushroom extracts, some thought essential fatty acids were valuable and others pointed out a variety of immune boosting supplements, but all of them praised the reputation of this one remarkable healing tea."

"What is it?" Mom prodded.

"It's called Flor·essence and it's an herbal formula based on an old Native Indian tea. After reading up on it I'm convinced this is something we should take a close look at."

"Why do you say that?" Dad quipped. "What makes it so special?"

"The remedy has stood the test of time and the dedication and reputation of the people associated with it is impeccable. For decades it has helped in the healing and recovery of thousands of cancer patients. Now its popularity has spread throughout the world, yet many people are still unaware of it."

"Please tell us more about it," Mom urged. Maybe it was the tone of my voice or a slight detection of confidence, but Mom and the rest of the family were all ears. I couldn't remember all of the details, so I proceeded to read from my notes:

"Back in the 1890s, an English woman who lived in a Northern Ontario mining town discovered a lump in her breast. There was an Indian settlement nearby where the lady and her husband visited an old Ojibwa medicine man to ask for his advice. The medicine man recommended a secret herbal potion that had been passed down from generation to generation. This holy drink was reputed to revitalize the body so it could once again be in harmony with the Great Spirit. At first, the couple was skeptical and opted to travel down to a hospital in Toronto for clinical tests. When she was diagnosed with breast cancer and amputation was advised, the couple decided to reconsider the sage advice of the medicine man and try his healing tea. It proved to be a blessing, for within a year of taking the tea the cancer disappeared and never returned."

"So she went around spreading the word about the miracle potion?" Dad interjected.

"Actually, news of the tea didn't surface until 1922 when the same lady was a patient at a hospital in the small town of Haileybury, Ontario. There was this head nurse named Rene Caisse who was busy doing her rounds and she stumbled upon this lady with a scarred breast. After the lady recounted the story of how her cancer was cured thirty years earlier by this potent tea, Rene Caisse was somewhat amazed and requested the names of the herbs. She had no idea how this chance discovery would consume the rest of her life. When Rene's aunt was diagnosed with terminal cancer of the liver and stomach a few years later, the opportunity unfolded to experiment with the herbs. The aunt's physician, Dr. R.O. Fisher, gave her only six months to live, so Rene traveled down to his clinic in Toronto and requested permission to test the tea out. This was Rene's favorite aunt and she didn't want to watch her suffer from the punishing effects of radium therapy. After drinking the herbal mixture for two months, the tumors began to shrink and the aunt recovered. She actually went on to live for another twenty years."

"Wow! This tea sounds too good to be true! Mom remarked.

"It certainly would make me stand up and take notice." I replied. "As a result, Rene Caisse and Dr. Fisher teamed up and commenced treating other cancer patients who had been given up by their doctors. Rene had to go out and collect the wild herbs herself and brew them overnight to make the tea. As it was common practice to administer liquid medicine hypodermically, they speculated they might experience further success if the tea was placed into ampoules and injected. The results were encouraging, as the condition of many patients improved remarkably. For the next two years, they continued treating terminally ill cancer patients, and even created a laboratory to conduct experiments on mice inoculated with human cancer. They discovered the best results could be obtained by injecting only one key herb, sheep sorrel, and administering the remaining herbs orally as an infusion. It was believed the sheep sorrel broke down the mass of malignant cells, and the other herbs helped purify the blood and carry off the destroyed tissue. News of their success blanketed the region, and other doctors started sending their hopeless cases to Rene for her miraculous remedy. One referral was a lady suffering from intestinal cancer as well as diabetes. To prevent potential complications, the patient agreed to temporarily discontinue her insulin injections while taking Rene's formula. After six months of treatment, she not only recovered from the cancer, but they found her diabetes had disappeared as well. One prominent physician, Sir Frederick Banting, heard about this case and concluded that the herbs must have stimulated the pancreas to function normally again."

"Wasn't he the co-discoverer of insulin?" Dad asked.

"Yes, in fact, years later he started investigating some of the case histories, and was so impressed that he invited Rene to join him and conduct further research on the tea at the Banting Institute, his facility in Toronto. However, Nurse Rene Caisse turned the offer down."

"I don't understand why she decided against it?" Dad piped in. "Dr. Banting was respected worldwide for his medical research. It would have been a major breakthrough."

"Over the years, Rene received several lucrative business proposals. She was offered large sums of money and operating capital to run a first-rate research clinic; but it would have meant signing over the rights to the herbal formula and abandoning all of her current patients while years of scientific tests were conducted to legitimize the life-saving properties of the tea. Rene might have seemed stubborn, although she possessed a generous heart and chose to heal and offer hope to the thousands of desperate patients afflicted with cancer. Instead of enjoying a rich and prestigious life, she devoted her time to helping the sick and living a rather humble existence."

"She seems like quite the humanitarian," Willow commented. "Didn't she accumulate a lot of money from her many patients?"

"Hardly, the medical authorities were repeatedly threatening to have her put in jail for treating people without a license or an approved remedy. At one point, eight doctors signed and sent in a petition to the Department of National Health and Welfare requesting that Rene be legally allowed to continue her work. They considered her remedy was safe and helped to relieve pain and prolong life. Since the patients were terminal and there was not much more the doctors could do for them, the Minister of Health gave his consent to Rene as long as she didn't charge money for her treatments."

"So licensed physicians and established medical practitioners could impose exorbitant fees for treatments that weren't effective, and she couldn't charge for this simple herbal formula that was so successful? How on earth was she supposed to survive?" Willow's response was tinged with anger and I sensed a piqued fascination with my parents regarding the events I was meticulously relating.

"Rene used to accept only donations for her services, but her dedication earned her a growing following of loyal supporters. She made the headlines when a major article was published about her in the Toronto Star newspaper. Then, Dr. A.F. Bastedo, a physician from Rene's hometown of Bracebridge, came to her aid. After one of his patients with terminal bowel cancer recovered following Rene's treatment, he solicited the mayor to allow her to utilize the unoccupied British Lion Hotel for a cancer clinic. The townspeople banded together and refurnished the building with an office, dispensary, reception area and five treatment rooms."

"That's so sweet!" Mom reemphasized her motto in a touching tone. "Always be a kind soul and life will be kind to you."

"There's a lot of truth in that, but Rene still persisted with her selfless mission and worked arduously day and night. From 1934 to 1942, she treated thousands of terminally ill patients from all walks of life. As in the past, they had previously been diagnosed with cancer and had already been subjected to conventional treatment. The historical accounts of how so many people recuperated while taking the herbal remedy are astonishing. Even Rene's 72 year old mother, who was diagnosed with inoperable liver cancer, completely recovered and lived long enough to celebrate her 90th birthday. Rene later stated that this repaid her for all of her work and the persecution she endured at the hands of the medical establishment."

"With all the generous offers coming in, she must have been guided by a higher power," Willow mused. "She stayed committed to her true course and never wavered. Nurse Caisse was some remarkable human being."

"That's why I find this whole story so intriguing, but it gets more interesting." I assured. "In 1937 a petition signed by 17,000 citizens was presented to the provincial legislature. Supporters were campaigning to the government to sanction Rene's cancer treatment. News about the miraculous healings spread further, and Rene was approached by a Chicago physician to work part-time in the department of Cancer Research Development at Northwestern University. Here she would be given thirty volunteer cancer patients to treat under the supervision of five doctors, and since there was no stipulation she divulge the formula, she consented. The research project went on for a year and a half, and the doctors concluded that the herbal remedy broke down tumors, helped relieve pain and prolonged the life of the patient. During this period, Rene was faced with a grueling schedule, her time splintered between treating people in Chicago, Toronto and her Bracebridge clinic."

"So was that research good enough? Did the government give her the green light to freely treat patients and charge for her services?" Mom asked.

"No. Despite the fact that more and more people sent in letters to the Premier and The Department of Health, many of them from prominent doctors." I had actually made copies of some of them and quickly pulled one from my stack of notes. "Let me read you this one from Dr. Benjamin Leslie Guyatt," I continued. "He was the curator of the University of Toronto's anatomy department and used to visit Rene's clinic on a regular basis."

"In most cases, distorted countenances became normal, and the pain reduced as treatment proceeded. The relief from pain is a notable feature, as pain in these cases is very difficult to control. On checking authentic cancer cases, it was found that hemorrhage was rapidly brought under control in many difficult cases; open lesions of lip and breast responded to treatment; cancer of the cervix, rectum and bladder have been caused to disappear; and patients with cancer of the stomach diagnosed by reputable physicians and surgeons have returned to normal activity. I do know that I have witnessed in this clinic a treatment which brings about restoration through destroying the tumor tissues and supplying that something which improves the mental outlook on life and facilitates reestablishment of physiological function."

"Then another petition with 55,000 signatures was circulated to the government, along with a private bill proposal from the Liberal Party to legalize Rene's work. This would enable Rene to treat patients before they were diagnosed as terminal and without the continued interference from the authorities. It seems the whole affair was tainted by politics, for shortly after, the Minister of Health was replaced by Harold Kirby, who was a staunch backer of modern medical science. He subsequently introduced a different bill into the legislature that urged the creation of a Royal Cancer Commission to look into the matter of 'unorthodox' cancer treatments. Of course, this would be composed of members of the Canadian College of Physicians and Surgeons.'"

"Boy, this is becoming a major event!" Willow exploded. "Not just for Rene but possibly for the protocol of how cancer would be treated in the future."

"Yes, and I bet the vast majority of the medical community perceived the initial proposed bill as a threat to their credibility," Dad added.

Not to be left out of the excitement, Mom squeezed in her own comment, "How could one small nurse possibly win against an influential giant like the medical establishment? It's like David versus Goliath!"

All three of them nodded for me to go on. "After a fierce debate in parliament, Rene's bill was defeated by just three votes. It just wasn't going to happen—passing the bill would have essentially endorsed Rene's treatment as a cure or respected remedy for cancer. When the Kirby bill was passed into law a few days later, Rene Caisse realized she would have to provide conclusive evidence to the Royal Cancer Commission on the merit of her treatment. Another stipulation of the bill was to fully disclose her herbal formula or run the risk of stiff fines and the possibility of imprisonment. Members of the commission traveled north to Bracebridge to investigate her clinic and, in the spring of 1939, held a public hearing at the Royal York Hotel in Toronto. Rene had 387 anxious patients ready to testify about their recovery from cancer while on her remedy. Only 49 were given the opportunity to speak. Unfortunately, the commission deflected many of the testimonials as either misdiagnosis or their cure possibly attributed to prior radium treatments. They wanted to conduct their own clinical tests and for Rene to submit her formula to them. She flatly refused."

"Good for her!" Willow declared. "Who knows what they would have done with the formula, and if their years of experiments on animals and various stages of disease would have been shelved due to some improper procedure or inconsistency. Rene had thousands of case studies and grateful patients and the commission refused to acknowledge them. Sometimes science blindly squints at the object in a test tube, but refuses to open its eyes at the living human proof standing before it."

"Well said, Willow. I believe Rene knew justice would not be served, at least not through the judiciary process. For awhile afterwards she kept her clinic open, but due to the ruling of the Royal Cancer Commission, interested patients found it increasingly difficult to supply Rene with a written diagnosis from their physician. Emotionally exhausted and fearing prosecution under the guidelines of the recent Kirby law, Rene decided to close her clinic in 1942."

"Her patients must have been devastated!"

"I'm sure most of them were, and who knows how their health endured since the herbal remedy was no longer accessible. Rene was tired of fighting and just needed to take a well deserved break. She and her husband moved to the small town of North Bay where they could relax in anonymity."

"I think we should all take a breather ourselves," Mom suggested. "Why don't we enjoy some lunch and then go for a stroll along the riverbank."

"A wonderful idea!" Willow agreed. "And it's nice to see you feeling a bit more motivated, Mom."

"This story is giving me some inspiration. I do hope it has a happy ending, Vincent."

I shot Mom a little smile but kept silent. Willow proceeded to reel in Calin from the neighbor's pond next door. Thank God he had befriended their little boy and didn't mind being stranded from our long discussions. While Mom and Dad whipped up a smorgasbord of appetizing sandwiches, I sliced up a plump and juicy watermelon and prepared some fresh lemonade. During the meal we listened to Calin's enchantment with the tiny turtles and goldfish as they silently mingled among the lily pads.

"I spotted seven goldfish and six turtles in all," he explained with delight. "They seemed pretty shy, but when we sprinkled in some food they suddenly went crazy."

"Sounds just like people. You give them something enticing and they behave in a completely different manner." Willow's remark probably sailed over Calin's head, but we knew what she was referring to.

"Perhaps it brings out the best in some people and the worst in others," I added.

Fishing vessels burdened with nets and glass buoys resembling gigantic marbles bobbed beside their moorings. Their hulls squeaked against the dock posts like scavenging seagulls as the swells from the sea rolled in and receded. As we walked beside the waterway that afternoon, I couldn't help but reflect how Rene's path was similar to the winding Fraser River nearing the completion of its long journey—the old and laden current soon to merge with the vast ocean where new waves of energy would direct its course.

As we wandered further along, we noticed the landscape gradually change. Where the inlet narrowed, there was still a scattering of dilapidated shacks that were rented out by solitary fishermen. A few of them had dragged up dead logs from the sandy shore to carve out crafts that could be sold in town. On the opposite side of the embankment was a marsh, and Dad was anxious to point out the red-winged blackbirds that made their nests amongst the reeds. It was soothing to see remnants of a simple world that had remained unscathed from the bulldozers and cookie-cutter cramping of housing developers.

While heading back we detected a stray dog following us, cautiously tailing thirty yards behind. Calin couldn't resist the temptation to pet it and knelt down while gently coaxing it to come nearer. "Come here boy, we won't hurt you. C'mon."

The dog slowly limped forward and we realized it was a Golden Retriever. It appeared friendly enough, so we didn't mind letting Calin offer it some affection.

"It seems so lonely," he said. "Maybe it's injured."

"I think the poor thing is just old," Willow remarked. "And it doesn't have any dog tags. Perhaps the owner just got tired of taking care of it."

"Can we take it back to the house, Mom?" Calin pleaded.

"That decision is up to your Grandpa and Grandma." Willow's eyes flickered imploringly at our parents. After a brief discussion, it was agreed to provide it with shelter, but they would place an ad in the local newspaper and try to locate its rightful owner. I wasn't crossing my fingers. Whoever the former custodian was, they obviously didn't display a whole lot of concern for their pet.

On the way home, we made a pit stop at a pet supply store to pick up some dog food and shampoo. Calin selected a stuffed toy to entertain his new found friend, but the poor animal was just too rundown to play. All of a sudden there was more than one patient to attend to in the household.

We all had a full day and, not long after supper, Willow tucked Calin into bed while Dad kindled the crackling blaze he ignited in the living room fireplace. We relaxed on the soft sofas to resume our discussion, and I was hit with the obvious question.

"So whatever happened to Nurse Caisse, and how did the formula evolve to where it is today?"

"After her husband died in 1948, Rene returned to Brace-bridge where she resumed a quiet life, although there were rumors that she occasionally treated ill patients in her home. In 1959, at the ripe age of 70, a crucial turning point occurred in Rene's career. She was approached by a fellow named Ralph Daigh, the vice president and publishing editor of True and other world famous magazines. They were interested in writing a story about Rene's life and her 'herbal cure' for cancer. Like so many others, Daigh first wanted to see further scientific investigation on the formula to prove its efficacy, and he knew of the perfect person to work with Rene to finally establish irrefutable credibility for her treatment. He proposed that Rene consider going to the Brusch Medical Center in Massachu-setts to collaborate on research under the supervision of Dr. Charles Brusch. She would retain the rights to her formula, and if clinical tests conducted on human cancer patients proved positive, a corporation would be created to make the remedy available to the public. Rene never hesitated."

"And who is Dr. Charles Brusch?" Dad inquired.

"Dr. Brusch was one of the most distinguished doctors in the United States at the time. Not only was he the close friend and personal physician of President John F. Kennedy, but he was the recipient of numerous awards and honors, both as a physician and humanitarian. Although his work in mainstream medicine was highly regarded, he was also a pioneer in the field of preventative medicine and had founded the first acu-puncture research center. It was no coincidence that he and Rene saw eye to eye."

"What were the results of the clinical studies conducted with Rene's herbal remedy?"

"After only three months of research on qualified cancer cases, Dr. Brusch and his colleagues concluded that clinically it reduced pain and caused a recession in the growth of the cancer. They also noticed that patients gained weight and their general health improved. Convinced that this natural and nontoxic remedy had merit, further experiments were conducted at the Brusch Medical Center for several years. Dr. Charles Brusch and Rene Caisse soon become legal partners in research and development. They consented on the rationale of refining the formula so that the key component no longer needed to be injected. Just like the original eight-herb brew of the Objiwa Indians, this perfected version could be taken orally, which made it possible for suffering patients to conveniently administer it themselves in the comfort of their own homes."

"So they truly shared the same desire of making the herbal remedy accessible to the public?" Mom asked.

"Yes. Rene and Dr. Brusch were both getting on in years and there was certainly no motive for fortune or amplified fame. They simply wished to serve suffering humanity.

Feeling confident in Dr. Brusch's research, Rene returned to Bracebridge, but continued to supply the herbs to his clinic. During this period, she was also involved with the Sloan-Kettering Cancer Center in New York where her treatment was tested on mice. These experiments, however, were poorly conducted and produced flawed results, so she ceased sending them her material."

"I bet that only helped solidify her trust in the professionalism and honorable intentions of Dr. Brusch," Willow surmised.

"It did indeed," I said. "In 1977, a series of articles were published in *Homemakers Magazine* that propelled Rene back into the Canadian limelight. Their reporters interviewed Rene and did a thorough investigation on the whole subject. The media had a field day. Once again, desperate cancer victims were pleading for this remarkable remedy, many flocking to her doorstep. The staff at Homemakers wished to assist Rene by trying to obtain a patent for the actual formula and establishing a trust to deal with the various agencies in order to make the remedy available to all who needed it. Due to her contractual arrangement with Dr. Brusch, she declined their offer."

"Boy, after all these years she still has all kinds of people reaching out to her," Mom commented. "They knew she had a true gift and were never going to leave her alone."

I was glad to see Mom so convinced and now understood that Rene's selfless mission would inspire others for centuries to come. We all felt a stitch of sadness when I explained that Rene Caisse passed away the following year at the age of 90. "Mourners traveled for miles to pay their respects to this giving soul, and a museum was eventually created to honor her extraordinary life. Her loyal friend and colleague, Dr. Charles Brusch, continued to discover impressive results with the refined eight-herb formula, and even healed his own cancer of the bowel in 1984. He was committed to ensuring that Rene's lifelong quest was more than just a passing dream."

A Dream Fulfilled

The answers we seek so often dangle before us.

Elaine Alexander was beside herself. Never in her twenty years as a radio broadcaster had she seen anything like it. She had previously interviewed the likes of Martin Luther King, Mohammed Ali and President Harry Truman, but the phone lines of her new talk show Stayin' Alive were now swamped more than ever with listeners responding to the declaration of her latest guest.

"I'm saying it's a cure!" Dr. Brusch confirmed. "I've seen it reverse and eliminate cancers at such a progressed state that nothing medical science currently has could have accomplished similar results. I wouldn't have believed it myself had I not seen it with my own eyes."

Dr. Brusch had never participated in a public radio interview before, but he had a strong conviction for Rene's dedicated work with the herbal remedy, and his admiration for the show's producer and host, Elaine Alexander, was oddly similar. Elaine had a sincere passion for educating and assisting others, especially in regards to serious health issues. Whether the approach was orthodox or alternative, she painstakingly researched thought-provoking health topics with the goal of enlightening her audience. In 1984, she invited a diverse group of leading experts to speak on her show, including Dr. Luc Montague, the French discoverer of the AIDS virus. The awareness of AIDS was just beginning to grow, but a natural cure for cancer was BIG news. Elaine became obsessed with learning more about the lifesaving tea and its benefit to mankind. She dug up newspaper archives, studied the healing properties of the herbs and interviewed a number of former patients who knew Rene and recovered from her treatment. The live airing with Dr. Brusch lasted two hours and was followed by pandemonium. Listeners who couldn't get through the jammed telephone lines to Stayin' Alive even drove out to the studio to speak with Elaine. These people had suffered dramatically from conventional cancer therapy, and as with Rene, they saw Elaine Alexander as a beacon of new hope.

"So Elaine kept the dream alive that Rene Caisse and Dr. Brusch had nurtured?" Willow asked. "But she wasn't a nurse or a doctor. How could she accommodate all those souls afflicted with cancer?"

"That was her biggest challenge," I responded. "Over the next couple of years, she interviewed Dr. Brusch four more times and continued featuring various aspects of the evolving Indian 'holy drink' on her show. Hundreds of people were pleading for this remedy she didn't even possess. Some eventually found out where she lived and commenced camping outside her house. Elaine was overwhelmed with all of their questions, but her devotion to helping them never wavered. She felt their pain and desperation and her heart reached out to them, laboring endless hours to tranquilize their agitated spirits. Replying to the ceaseless onslaught of phone calls and letters took her to the brink of exhaustion—until she came up with a brilliant idea."

"I can't wait to hear this!" Mom exclaimed. "So often the weary seem to hit a dead end when, all of a sudden, a door of divine providence opens up for them."

"Before I explain, I have something I wish to show you." I had anxiously been waiting for this moment to indulge Mom with my surprise, which I quickly retrieved from my room. The box was ornately covered with festive wrapping, and when Mom saw it was a gift, her face transitioned into a glittering glow.

"How thoughtful of you, Vincent! I can't imagine what it could be—it's not even a special occasion."

"Perhaps it is a special occasion. Perhaps it takes a predicament to make us realize how precious we all are to each other. Now go ahead, open it up."

Mom enthusiastically unraveled the packaging and couldn't contain herself. "I can't believe my eyes—it's the miracle tea!"

Six bottles of Flor·essence were hastily pulled from the box and everyone scrutinized the labels.

"This is the outcome of Elaine's brainstorm," I explained. "Instead of fighting for approval from the government and medical authorities, she realized the remedy could be made available to the public just by offering it as a simple detoxifying herbal tea. As long as no disease claims are made, the product can be legally sold as a dietary supplement."

"So you purchased this at the local health food store?" Willow asked.

"Yes, it's readily available at natural food outlets all over the world now. In fact, the Canadian manufacturer is located less than an hour's drive from here."

"I see it is made by a company called Flora—it's obvious that's where the name originated. But how did the formula in Dr. Brusch's possession get to the stage it is now and why wasn't this avenue of approach pursued earlier?" Willow's questions were valid and I reassessed my notes before replying.

"Dr. Brusch had continued experimenting with the tea, but only in a research capacity. Like Rene, he wanted to make the remedy widely available, but assumed the medical establishment wouldn't legitimize it until more and more controlled clinical studies were completed. And back then I doubt if they ever would have embraced such a simple and natural approach to healing. Treating the whole person with non-invasive herbal formulas, regenerative diets and subtle energy balancing just wasn't in the mindset of conventional medicine. They resorted to the more aggressive tactics of surgery, radiation, toxic chemicals and drugs to combat disease."

"They still do today, and in many cases it is probably warranted, but I certainly wouldn't describe it as a health care system," Mom stipulated.

"Perhaps Dr. Brusch was ahead of his time," I concluded. "When Elaine conferred with him about her idea, he was convinced it was the perfect solution. Natural health products were finally booming due to a receptive public. In 1988 he quickly made Elaine a partner and signed over the legal ownership of the eight-herb formula, as well as the rights to other related formulas developed over the years by Rene Caisse and himself. Elaine was honored to be entrusted with a remedy that could save thousands, possibly millions of lives, but she knew it meant the end of her career in radio. Her challenge now was to find a reputable company to manufacture and market the tea."

"What a lucky break! Flora was practically in her own backyard!" Willow announced.

"Yes, but being the staunch investigator she was, it took Elaine almost four years to locate the ideal company."

"Why did it take her so long to find someone to produce the tea?" Willow inquired.

"Dr. Brusch had only been experimenting with the remedy on a handful of patients for research purposes. Now that the tea was going public, it would require an established herbal manufacturer capable of producing it en masse and shipping it out to distribution points around the globe. The company had to specialize in preparing both dry and liquid botanicals, and have state-of-the-art production facilities that could guarantee an end product of the finest quality. They also had to have access to a huge volume of premium grade raw plant material. After investigating a number of potential companies, Flora seemed to be the perfect fit. Not only were they an award-winning and reputable manufacturer, they also had their own farms that specialized in biological cultivation and were third-party certified organic."

"Ah! I see now it was a much more complicated process," Willow said. "She must have been so relieved after she learned about Flora?"

"When Elaine Alexander met with the owner, Thomas Greither, she was duly impressed. The level of integrity and the spiritual vision behind the company was instantly apparent. She felt confident they consistently fulfilled their commitment of providing exceptional remedies to the consumer. Even the German parent company, Salus Haus, was founded way back in 1916 by Thomas' grandfather, Dr. Otto Greither, and has since become one of the world leaders in manufacturing herbal teas and tonics. The Greither family presently owns organic farmlands throughout Bavaria, Chile and North America."

"They sound like they've really mastered their craft," Dad stated. "So Rene's dream did come true after all? But we still haven't come to a consensus on which mode of treatment is best for your mother."

"Whatever we decide, Flor·essence is gentle on the body and very safe when used on its own or as an adjunct with other types of treatment."

"After everything I've just heard, I have no reservations about taking it right away," Mom declared.

"I agree," Willow and I echoed in unison.

Dad could only smile in approval. "At a time like this, it's probably a Godsend. Just like all the birds I once never noticed, there are still so many things to discover. Good work, Vincent. I believe you've resurrected us all with a ray of renewed hope."

The Way Of Nature

Everything we need exists in nature.

Early next morning Mom and I rushed to the kitchen to prepare her first dose of Flor·essence. I followed the directions and boiled two ounces of filtered water and added it to the same volume of the liquid formula.

"It doesn't taste bad at all," she said. "I thought it was going to taste like some horrid medicine."

"It says to sip it slowly and drink it at least thirty minutes before breakfast. You should also take another serving on an empty stomach before going to bed each night."

"I'm just so grateful Flor·essence is so readily available now, Vincent."

"You wouldn't believe what happened, Mom. Just around the time Flora was given the green light to manufacture the healing tea, a feature article titled "Keeping Hope Alive" was printed in the *Vancouver Sun* newspaper. It profiled the work of Rene Caisse and her success in treating cancer patients with the herbal concoction, and it highlighted Elaine Alexander's continuing involvement with the remedy. Once again, a huge wave of interest was generated, but this time the formula was easily accessible to the public."

"And this time there was no conflict with the government or medical authorities?"

"Not at all, but afterwards numerous competitors jumped on the bandwagon and came out with their version of the tea. Many claimed they had the original remedy, including the smaller four-herb formula known as Essiac™. All kinds of controversy erupted, but Flora did a remarkable job of assuring the consumer that they had the authentic version perfected over the years by Rene Caisse and Dr. Brusch. Elaine Alexander even went on lecture tours and was interviewed on numerous radio shows, always carefully explaining how Flor·essence supports the body's own healing ability and clarifying how the precise percentage of each herb is so important in providing the optimum benefit. Her effort and inspiration helped make this lifesaving tea available in over fifty countries around the planet."

"Bravo! Bravo! It gives me faith that with enough sincere effort just about anything is possible, Vincent."

Just then we were surprised to overhear some voices out by the patio. Sure enough, Dad was out back educating Calin about the various birds he had seen. Calin was struggling to steady these high-powered binoculars while peering at a pair of blue-tinted birds.

"Just like clockwork," Dad stated. "Those two Steller's jays hang out by that old apple tree around the same time every morning. In a few hours from now, a gang of mischievous crows will be clashing about that mountain ash tree, and right around supper, a troop of black-capped chickadees will start chirping away in that bush beside the garage."

"But how do you know they'll be there?" Calin asked.

"Because they always are—just like the Big Dipper appears at a specific place in the sky, or daffodils blossom at certain times each spring. By closely observing the different kinds of birds, I have a pretty good idea when to expect them. Most of the time I can even tell the type of behavior they will exhibit and exactly where to find them."

"You can predict that, Grandpa?"

"Prediction is being able to foretell an event will happen because you understand the nature of things. For instance, during their breeding season in spring and summer, robins typically hunt on the ground for earthworms and insects. The parents stick close together and remain near the nest, but in the fall and winter months, they switch their search to a diet of berries and fruit, and it is common to see them flocking together with other robins in the same bush or tree. Only that robin with the brick-red breast over there likes to perch itself on the broken limb of that cottonwood tree."

"Why does it always sit in that spot?" Calin asked.

"It's keeping a watchful eye out for its newborn. The fledglings reside in a nest on the downspout at the corner of the roof, and from that vantage point the adult can see if they are safe. I imagine it claimed the broken limb as a lookout, and that robin isn't going to let anything take it over."

"Did you collect any of their pretty blue eggshells?"

"Sorry Calin. After the babies hatched, the adult flew off with the shells in its bill and dropped them far from the nest."

"Why did it do that?"

"Because God's creatures are innately intelligent—if the eggshells were dropped close to the nest, a predator could sense there are babies nearby and attack them. Even the young ones know when it is time to leave the nest and begin exploring the skies above. They don't attend flying school or receive any survival training, yet they are guided by their own natural instincts."

"Boy, those two sure seem to be hitting it off!" The voice came from behind us and we switched our attention 180° to see Willow in these psychedelic pajamas sporting an exuberant grin on her face. She couldn't conceal her delight in discovering her son's intrigue with the many facets of bird watching.

"A future ornithologist if I ever saw one!" I declared. "But how long have you been standing there?"

"Actually, I just got here. I was observing Dad and Calin from the bedroom and then I heard somebody clamoring around in here. What are you both up to?"

"Mom's enjoying her first serving of Flor·essence. Want to try some?"

"Why don't we all have some," Willow suggested. "We can make a toast to Mom's health and to Calin's future success in the field of biological sciences."

"He certainly displays a keen interest in nature," I said. "But doesn't he indicate that back home?"

"We live in such a concrete jungle back east. Apart from the odd TV show or trip to the zoo, I'm just not used to seeing that side of Calin. To be honest with you, I kind of miss a greener environment myself. It reminds me of the days we used to play in Granny's garden or run around in the park."

"The feeling is mutual, Willow. This modern world has become so artificial—but no matter how much mankind tries, he still can't reproduce a real flower, or a ladybug, or even a simple blade of grass. God's creation holds a mystery we will never unravel. One can only sit back in awe and appreciate the miracle within all living things."

"Perhaps that is something the Ojibwa Indians and other traditional societies understood," Willow added. "They bowed down with a reverence for the wonders of nature. The whole herb or a unique combination of herbs together, could provide a very effective and powerful means of healing the individual. There is wisdom inherent in the whole plant and the body knows best how to utilize it and replenish itself."

"If only people could realize how synthetic pills are foreign to the body. Pharmaceutical drugs commonly contain only one isolated substance. Even if it is sometimes derived from a plant, this chemical compound is not buffered by the other naturally occurring phytonutrients, vitamins, minerals and essential oils present in the original plant. As a result, the concentrated drug can be quite harsh and prone to cause severe side effects."

"I agree, Vincent. It seems major pharmaceutical corporations deliberately isolate a medicinal compound and synthetically modify it so they can claim it as their own proprietary drug. This allows them to market it under some fancy name only they can exclusively use and sell it for a specific ailment."

"Yes, and the money they recoup for the promise it delivers pays for the millions of dollars in research funds necessary to have it approved by the FDA—and they know that everything beyond that will reap huge profits for the company."

"You guys make me want to throw away all my pills," Mom declared.

I realized our conversation sounded a little threatening, especially to someone just recently acquainted with a new paradigm of health. "Mom, we're only saying that drugs should be looked upon with more skepticism, whether used long-term or temporarily. True healing comes from not just suppressing the symptom, but more importantly, from balancing and revitalizing the whole person."

"Modern medicine has come such a long way," Willow added. "And the recent advances in new pharmaceuticals, surgical techniques and innovative technology have helped so many people. In many circumstances it is completely necessary, particularly in the case of accidents or immediate life-threatening issues. However, in only treating the symptom, the underlying cause of the disease is ignored and the proper healing process is circumvented. The overall condition of the physical body, the mental and emotional attitude of the patient, and above all, the spiritual wellness of the individual are so often left to flounder."

"So what do you suggest I should do?" Mom asked.

"You and Dad should decide on the type and degree of conventional treatment you wish to pursue, but embarking on a positive path of vibrant living is something we should all participate in. During this intense week of research, Willow and I discovered so many new aspects of health and healing—and it's only the tip of the iceberg. We realize we are all getting older and any one of us is susceptible to some serious illness or unforeseen event that could disrupt our life. So many people are caught off guard and their first reaction is one of fear—they fall into an emotional tailspin, they play the poor victim, they become drug dependent, or they rush to their doctor or therapist to save them. Few people prepare themselves to master the changing demands that life deals out, yet we know we must one day confront them."

"Your bout with cancer has given us all an opportunity to approach our lives with a fresh perspective," Willow remarked. "We can take it slow, taking one step at a time. After doing some further reading, I believe the first thing to consider is undergoing a detoxification regime."

"Why is that so important, dear?"

"Because none of us are immune to the chemical pollutants in the environment or the thousands of preservatives in our food supply. Sulfites, nitrates, synthetic dyes, BHA, BHT, MSG and numerous acids or acetates contaminate most of the items on the dinner table. They are often used to retard packaged food from spoiling, to inhibit the growth of bacteria and other microbes, or to sustain the color and enhance the flavor of different grocery items, but many are suspected cancer contributing agents."

Willow and I were both starting to perceive the body as a precious ecosystem. After pondering her comment, I added my own analogy. "The bloodstream is like an organic river transporting essential elements to the cells and organs, and dumping chemicals into it is synonymous with poisoning a river. Year after year, these toxins accumulate and inflict untold damage to our own inner environment and then we wonder why disease sets in. Flor·essence, however, identifies and gathers in harmful toxins, breaks them down and discharges them from the body."

Our conversation was interrupted when Calin burst through the door. "I just saw a hummingbird, Mom! It kept hovering right in front of me."

"It was a rufous hummingbird," Dad clarified. "I think it was attracted to Calin's red shirt."

"That's enough showing off for one day, Mr. Bird Expert." Mom smiled and gestured for them to sit down at the kitchen table. "I assume you both built up a hearty appetite for breakfast?"

"How about some coffee with fried eggs and bacon," Dad requested.

"Since when did you start putting eggs and bacon in your coffee?"

"Smart Aleck!"

It was nice to see the light-hearted interplay between Mom and Dad, and I was proud to see Mom's continued emphasis on a healthier menu.

"Perhaps I should prepare everyone some poached eggs, steamed broccoli and bran muffins—and some freshly-squeezed grapefruit juice wouldn't hurt." Mom explained how we were just discussing the importance of following a more health-conscious lifestyle. "What were you saying about the properties of Flor·essence, Vincent?"

"The formula as a whole can help keep toxins and free radicals at bay, enabling our cells and various organs to function at peak efficiency. Perhaps this is the reason it's so revitalizing."

"Maybe we should give some to that sack of lazy bones over there!" Dad pointed to the retriever curled up in a ball beside Calin's chair. And even though his suggestion was made in jest, it held some validity.

"That's not a bad idea! I remember reading how therapeutic it is for animals." Before I could elaborate, Calin enthusiastically cut in.

"What a swell name! If you keep the dog, can we call him Lazy Bones?"

"The name certainly seems appropriate," Dad remarked. "I'll make you a deal, Calin. If nobody claims him over the next five days, then we'll make Lazy Bones a permanent addition to the family—but in the meantime, you have to feed him and give him the proper daily dose of Flor·essence."

"Deal!"

"Since the formula is safe for both humans and their pets, just what are the properties of the individual ingredients, anyways?" Mom asked.

While Mom and Willow were busy arranging breakfast, I leafed through some of the literature I had collected and read the following out loud:

"Sheep sorrel helps counteract toxins and oxygenates tissues at the cellular level. It contains several effective antioxidants such as Vitamin C, Vitamin A and flavonoids. It also provides strong immune support and reduces inflammation.

Burdock root is an excellent blood purifier and contains a proven anti-cancer agent called arctigenin, which has been shown in scientific studies to possess marked anti-tumor activity. Other research has revealed the herb decreases mutations in cells exposed to toxic chemicals.

Slippery elm bark is renowned for soothing the digestive tract by virtue of its high mucilage content.

By balancing pH in the GI tract, it heals and protects inflamed or irritated membranes.

Turkish rhubarb root has been used since ancient times and assists in normalizing bowel movements, cleansing the liver and detoxifying the colon. It increases peristalsis by gently stimulating the muscular layer of the bowel and so is considered a safe and effective laxative.

Red clover is a popular antioxidant and blood purifier that facilitates the elimination of wastes via the kidneys, colon and skin. Recent research indicates that red clover contains anti-microbial compounds which help battle several bacterial, fungal and viral infections.

Blessed thistle contains a bitter-tasting compound called cnicin, which increases the flow of gastric juices, thereby relieving indigestion and headaches associated with liver congestion.

Kelp is a marine plant saturated with a spectrum of valuable minerals, including iodine for healthy thyroid function and metabolism. The alginates in kelp are beneficial for cleansing the intestines, preventing the absorption of heavy metals and protecting the body against radiation.

Watercress is a rich source of chlorophyll, vitamins and alkalizing minerals, and is an ideal blood purifier and diuretic. It was traditionally used as a restorative for those suffering from chronic conditions."

"That mighty group can play on my team any day!" Mom exclaimed.

"They sure work well in unison together," I confirmed. "As you know, the synergistic effect of the full eight-herb blend is much more powerful than taking the herbs individually.

Flor·essence is beneficial for just about anything from A to Z."

"From arthritis to zits?"

"Something like that, Calin." I chuckled, realizing the lightness of the moment was good medicine and provided a veil for our deeper concerns. I continued with my explanation:

"So many conditions manifest when the body is thrown off balance. A healthy individual has built-in defense mechanisms that instinctively react to combat toxins that overload the system, but someone congested with sub-par health just isn't able to handle all the poisons that accumulate over time. As a result, the delicate pH balance in the body becomes disrupted, gradually leading to inflammation and irritation of the mucous membranes. This may trigger a condition known as *leaky gut syndrome*, which means these membranes become porous, allowing unwanted toxins to re-enter the bloodstream from the colon. If left unchecked, it can eventually cause the immune and endocrine systems to shut down, resulting in various auto-immune disorders such as diabetes or chronic fatigue syndrome. When these types of dysfunctions are allowed to persist, the DNA repair system falters and cell mutation occurs."

"I think I get the picture," Mom said. "Maybe the tumors associated with cancer are simply the body's intuitive reaction to localize these damaged cells. But why does cancer manifest at different places in each person?"

"Perhaps it is the tissue area that is genetically the weakest. Perhaps it is the place where a person habitually holds on to their emotions, which is another tangent of healing I'm just beginning to explore. We've been focusing so much on Flor·essence, but it is just one tool. I really believe there are many tools the universe provides, and we should commit ourselves to those we are most drawn to."

A Delicate Balance

Perpetual balance is instrumental to life.

O ver the following week, Willow and I continued combing
for other holistic measures and we were both anxious to
untangle our findings. There was such a diverse range of rejuvenating diets and health supplements, and we discovered the
options were about as varied and controversial as conventional
medicine. We decided to keep our game plan simple.

"After reviewing a wide selection of books on nutrition,
I believe one of the best strategies is to incorporate raw vegetable juices."

"And why is that, Willow?"

"Because only freshly pressed juices offer a concentration
of vitamins, minerals, phytonutrients and fiber in a superior
format. Unlike man-made dietary supplements, which are
isolated from nature and prepared in a lab or manufacturing facility, fresh juices are alive with a complete spectrum
of naturally occurring nutrients. As people get older, their
own supply of digestive enzymes diminishes and it becomes
harder to metabolize the foods they eat. Raw juices are not
only easier to assimilate, but they also provide an abundance
of enzymes and oxygen—and research indicates that cancer
cells can't thrive in the presence of oxygen."

"It certainly is much better than cooked or packaged
food!" I declared.

"Cooking not only destroys valuable enzymes, but it dis-
rupts the molecular structure of the vitamins and minerals
and many are damaged in the process. The perfect matrix of
nutritional elements in fresh juice works synergistically, just
like the herbs in Flor·essence, and right now Mom needs all

the regenerating power she can get."

"You don't have to convince me. Fresh juice and wholesome food seems to be the best—the minute something is cooked or spliced up into little pieces, it slowly begins to oxidize or decompose. Just look how quickly an apple starts to brown or a fragment of lettuce starts to wilt shortly after it is cut up."

"I knew you would understand, Vincent. I just hope Mom respects our recommendations. Thankfully, there are a number of inspiring stories by nutritional doctors who were strong advocates of fresh juice therapy and raw foods."

"Such as?"

"Dr. Norman Walker became a living endorsement for fresh vegetable juices by rehabilitating his health and reaching the age of 109. He designed his own elaborate juicer and created numerous fresh juice recipes geared to cleansing the colon and improving specific health conditions. The late author and renowned nutritionist, Dr. Paavo Airola, also influenced thousands of people worldwide to embrace the exceptional healing benefits of raw juices. He recommended periodic juice fasting to help eliminate toxic wastes and dead cells that crystallize in the joints and accumulate in various body tissues. Juice fasting not only stimulates new cell building, but normalizes many metabolic functions and accelerates energy levels."

"Sounds like something everyone should consider. Too many people try to artificially jumpstart their sluggishness with caffeine or soda pop laced with sugar, but I know these can be detrimental in the long run."

Willow and I only had to reflect on our own hectic lifestyles to realize how common it is to fall into conventional habit patterns. It was time for us to begin incorporating some of the messages we were fortunate to come across. Willow continued with her synopsis of the pioneers who pointed the way for a healthier mankind.

"Then there was Professor Arnold Ehret, the German naturopath who wrote the *Mucusless-Diet Healing System*, which promises a path to vibrant health through proper systematic fasting and a moderate diet rich in ripe fruits and vegetables. Through his own lifelong experiments, he believed one of the fundamental causes of disease was due to the build-up of too much mucus, which congests the body and becomes a breeding ground for harmful pathogens. Ehret stressed that mucus-forming foods such as milk, eggs, meat and starches are also acid-producing and eventually lead to inflammation and irritation. Alkaline foods that are mucus free, help bind with and neutralize these harmful acids, and their high fiber content acts like a broom to mechanically sweep away toxic debris and poisons from the colon and digestive tract."

Willow was holding a copy of his book and she flipped it open to show me a photograph of the professor. I was astounded at how vibrant he looked. "Wow! That's a great visual for anyone aspiring to be healthy—you can tell he really practiced what he preached. He must have been an inspiration to so many people in his day. How long did he live, Willow?"

"Unfortunately, at the peak of his life, Professor Ehret accidentally slipped and fractured his skull. He died instantly at the age of 56. But there are so many individuals whose triumphant battle with their own illness became a blessing to others. The last health educator I want to mention is Dr. Ann Wigmore, founder of the Hippocrates Institute."

"The Wheatgrass Lady," I acknowledged. "I heard about her at the health food store."

"That's right. She prescribed wheatgrass juice and "live" or sprouted foods to help her heal herself and a loyal following of cancer patients. The vital force and concentrated nourishment in unprocessed "living" foods aid in the body's natural ability to regenerate itself. In fact, the chlorophyll molecule found in wheatgrass and other green foods is very similar to a molecule of hemoglobin, which transports oxygen in human blood. Oxygenating the body with a shot of green juice every day is like getting a small blood transfusion."

"Yes, but I don't know if Mom would be that receptive to wheatgrass juice. I tried a few ounces of it and it's pretty strong tasting. If she's open to it, that's fine. We just don't want to scare her off and have her thinking we've suddenly become health fanatics."

"We know these types of therapies would be so beneficial for her. What do you suggest?" Willow inquired.

"There are a number of concentrated green powders I came across at the health food store that contain combinations of organic wheatgrass, barley grass, alfalfa, spirulina and chlorella, and these super foods can simply be stirred into the freshly-pressed juice or added to a nutritional shake."

"So they are easier on the palate?"

"Much easier, Willow, and a lot more convenient! Another important element lacking in the average North American diet is EFAs."

"EFAs?"

"Essential fatty acids! EFAs are abundant in fish oils as well as flax, sunflower, sesame and other raw seeds. They are necessary for a variety of body functions including proper cellular oxygenation of body tissues, balancing blood glucose, stimulating digestion and supporting cardiovascular health, as well as strengthening the immune and nervous system. Thanks to the pioneering research efforts of Dr. Johanna Budwig, flax gained considerable recognition for its therapeutic role in helping cancer patients. She discovered that the majority of her severely ill patients were missing EFA-containing lipoproteins in their blood. Giving them a diet rich in flax was instrumental in their healthy recovery. Dr. Budwig's work and the amazing benefits of flax were later profiled in the book *Fats That Heal, Fats That Kill,* by Udo Erasmus. Since most of the supermarket oils are mass-produced with bleaching agents and intense heat that destroys the sensitive fatty acids, Udo pioneered the production of fresh, unrefined oils prepared without the damaging effects of heat and oxygen. He actually has his own line of flax-based EFA-rich oils that can also be added to fresh vegetable juice."

"There are just so many natural weapons out there, Vincent. How could one ever retreat from the war against cancer?"

"The common denominator each of these health enthusiasts seem to share is their deep devotion, understanding and faith in nature's pharmacy to purify and rejuvenate the whole body. Most people are aware of which foods are life-supporting, such as pure water, herbal teas, fresh fruits and vegetables, sprouts and whole grains. And most people are aware of which items can be life-depleting if consumed too much, such as meat, dairy products, starches, coffee, alcohol and packaged food. It's not rocket science! The problem is that most people struggle with committing to the time and discipline required to reverse disease symptoms and achieve sustained levels of optimum health. It's too easy to rely on pills or another facet of medical treatment. It's too easy to fall back into old diet and lifestyle patterns, especially if other family members and friends are unwilling to implement changes. There's only one solution, Willow—we need to all do it together."

"But you and I will be heading home back east soon, and even though Mom is starting to eat better, I don't know if Dad is ready for all this."

"Maybe I can instill some influence on them. Lately, I have been giving it a lot of thought and I've made the decision to move back here. Hopefully, I can stay with Mom and Dad for a few months until I get my bearings. My journalist work can be done from just about anywhere and I'm long overdue for my own revitalizing health program. I can help Mom continue preparing a variety of wholesome meals we can all enjoy. And even from a distance, you can phone or e-mail us with your latest health findings or experiences. The more we all participate, the more we'll motivate one another."

"That's very noble of you, Vincent. Have you expressed your intentions of relocating back home with them? Do you think they'll both go for it?"

"Yes, no and yes!"

"Sorry?"

"Yes, it might be considered noble. No, I haven't told them about my decision. And yes, I'm confident I can sway them to adhere to a substantial improvement in their diet—as long as it is sensible and doesn't become too extreme. Unless someone is on some self-enlightening mission, it is far too impractical to expect them, or myself, to achieve the pinnacle of health by only consuming freshly-pressed juices and raw foods, just as it is unnecessary to experience spirituality by sitting in a cave. We would most likely alienate ourselves and become socially isolated in the process. Each of us has to find our own comfort zone. I don't believe there is anything wrong with having an occasional glass of wine with dinner or ingesting moderate portions of eggs, pasta or milk, as long as we compensate the diet with a majority of high-vibrational alkaline foods. It's all a question of balance."

"I guess that's the trick! Nature herself remains in perpetual balance. A simple atom has a field of circulating electrons balanced by a core of stable protons, just as our solar system is composed of rotating planets balanced around a stable sun. It reminds me of the harmonious interplay between yin and yang."

"Yes, if Mom can't relate to positive and negative forces or acid versus alkaline balance, she definitely understands the value of not under watering or over watering her flowers."

"Good point, Vincent! But it is imperative we convince her about committing to daily live juice therapy."

"Imperative?"

"Yes, I've already purchased the juicer!"

Willow and I took a well deserved break and spent an amusing hour playing with Calin and Lazy Bones. Lazy Bones was awkwardly bumping into furniture or sliding across the polished floor as he scrambled after a stuffed teddy bear we kept tossing him. We could see the Flor·essence was taking effect. The resurrected retriever was friskier than ever and his once droopy tail now waggled nonstop with excitement. It only made the sunken hush when Mom and Dad traipsed in seem all the more opposite.

"The biopsy results?" I asked.

"They discovered the tumor is malignant."

Although we had all prepared and reconciled our fears with calmness, and although we had done our homework regarding a kind of test paper we knew was destined for an F, to hear those frightening words brought all the turbulence back again. The pink puffs circling Mom's eyes were evident, and Dad let out a stifled sigh before elaborating on the details.

"We still don't know how serious it is. They're not sure if it has metastasized to any of the surrounding lymph nodes or not."

"So what are you going to do?" Willow asked.

"We had a lengthy discussion with Dr. Shepherd, and at this point we're leaning towards a lumpectomy, which is an operation that only removes the tumor and some of the nearby tissue. He recommends following up the surgery with radiation treatment, but that may not even be necessary. Dr. Shepherd is open to sitting down with all of us in a few days and reviewing other options."

"Radiation therapy can be a nightmare!" I emphasized. "What are the other options?"

"There are many, but we narrowed it down to three reasonable options that are worthwhile considering. The first option is that we forego the radiation therapy after your mom's surgery and consider hormone treatment such as tamoxifen. Her biopsy test indicated the presence of cancer feeding estrogen-receptors in the tissue, and hormone therapy can induce an estrogen deprivation state at the tumor level. In one study involving 600 women profiled in the *New England Journal of Medicine*, it indicated that women your mom's age who were taking tamoxifen after a lumpectomy had the same five-year survival rate as those who were treated with radiation after the lumpectomy. A second option is to have a sentinel lymph node biopsy performed along with the lumpectomy."

"What does that mean?" Willow asked.

"It's a new technique that focuses on only removing and examining the sentinel lymph node, which is the first node receiving the drainage from the breast. If they find this node to be healthy, the chance of discovering cancer in any of the remaining lymph nodes is rare and minimizes the need for full axillary lymph node dissection. There is a much lower risk of painful side effects such as lymphedema, which often accompanies the removal of all the nodes in the underarm area."

"And the third option?" I inquired.

"The last option involves having the lumpectomy performed, and then weighing the risks and benefits of incorporating Flor·essence along with other holistic therapies. Mom and I agree that integrating natural treatments can only help, but we will feel much more comfortable if Dr. Shepherd is convinced that this approach is safe and carried through with insight, care and conviction."

"At the very least, these options are a lot less drastic than undergoing a mastectomy and combining radiation or chemotherapy." Willow followed up her comment by reiterating the details of our previous discussion, and then brought out the juicer she had recently purchased. It didn't take a fortune teller to perceive how serious we were.

"What do you think, son? Do you sincerely believe that juice therapy, a rejuvenating diet and the herbal tonic can cure your mom?"

"They're absolutely invaluable, Dad, but after all the information we've amassed and all the research we've poured through and processed, I'm not sure if I believe in an ultimate cure. There is only a cause—and a course of action that diligently addresses the cause and redeems the physical, emotional and spiritual equilibrium of the individual. We just need to proceed now with common sense."

"And what does your common sense tell you?"

"That it's not sensible to cripple the cells with chemotherapy or radiation. Past civilizations survived for centuries without them. That it's not sensible to disorient the system with hormones like tamoxifen. I came across a report which revealed one prosperous company that manufactures this controversial drug also produces pesticides and other environmental carcinogens. That's like purchasing your precious jewelry back from the same thief who stole them from you. I don't even consider it sensible to flood the body with scores of refined supplements. The human body is the most amazing creation I can think of. I believe it will respond best if we nourish it gently with the pure gifts that God created and nature so miraculously provides."

"So you and Willow prefer option three?"

"Yes, we believe the impetus should be placed on healing rather than treating the disease, but more importantly, what do you and Mom think is the best approach?"

Mom and Dad both looked at one another quizzically, and then Mom finally spoke up.

"Cancer is so complicated and we don't know if there is one exclusive solution. I agree with you both that nature has the power to magically repair and restore the body, but I also have to weigh the advice of Dr. Shepherd. I only hope I can maintain the necessary discipline to win my life back."

"Don't worry, Mom, whatever you choose I'll be standing right here beside you." When I indicated my intention of moving back to Steveston, our parent's subdued spirit soared with renewed optimism. Mom's eyes filled with tears again, but unlike before, they sprang from a fountain of joy.

Healing Thoughts

Disease is a manifestation of the mind.

The waves felt foreign, yet soothing, as if caressing some Caribbean shore. Golden sunlight shimmered upon the aquamarine surface and reflected like prisms off the school of rainbow fish below. Mom calmly sat in the back of a boat while Dad and I guided it through the waist deep water—he pulling on the starboard side and me pulling on the opposite. Mom was gazing at the stars above like some enraptured tourist, yet a lone tear trickled from her eye. Stars in the daytime sky, I asked? Then I awoke from the dream.

Perhaps my mind was playing games, hallucinating on the meeting scheduled that morning with Dr. Shepherd. We were all exhausted, pondering over the pages of data we had unearthed and analyzed to no end. I could slightly overhear Mom and Dad's discussion continuing into the wee hours of the night. Mom's cancer treatment was starting to seem surreal—the challenging experience as much for our learning as for hers. Did our endorsement for the type of therapy offer hopeful relief or compound the pressure of the whole dilemma? Mom was now faced with the predicament of deliberating between the wishes of her children and the recommendation of her doctor. Could both the conventional and the holistic approach find some common ground? When the outcome of the present choice before us is unknown, do we relinquish our fate to the stars?

The next day, we all piled into Dad's car and headed out to the clinic. It was still a blue Chevy, but the old dinosaur had long since been replaced with an updated model. Although Dad had already echoed the particulars of their previous meeting,

Dr. Shepherd carefully reviewed the conventional treatment options to all of us, pinpointing the rationale and repercussions of each. He put up a convincing argument supporting a series of radiation sessions following the lumpectomy, and how modern technology and application have improved the survival rates of patients. When Willow and I countered back with our objections and concerns, particularly the fatigue, appetite suppression and skin reactions Mom would most likely have to suffer through, he politely listened. He didn't try to deny the risks and side-effects involved, but simply stated the facts. We were surprised many of the natural therapies we shared with him were proposals he had heard before. However, he actually admitted to receiving only a miniscule amount of education regarding nutrition and alternative cancer treatments. Dr. Shepherd admired the intensive research we had conducted and commended us on selecting a health strategy that was based on practical principles.

"Life offers no guarantees, no matter what we choose. The courage it takes to remain dedicated to the choices we make, regardless of the opinions of others, is often more admirable than the choices themselves." The doctor peered straight at Mom with encouraging eyes, implying the ultimate decision rested on her tiny shoulders.

It seems Mom was a partisan of both sides. Maybe the inspiration for her decision was based less upon her heart and more from some higher guidance. Either way, she addressed us with a confident clarity. "I respect the wishes of Vincent and Willow and will commit to following a holistic regime. I now understand that if my day-to-day actions can contribute to a disease, then my day-to-day actions can help heal me. I also respect the proposed options presented by you, Dr. Shepherd, and have decided to undergo the sentinel lymph node biopsy along with the lumpectomy. The sentinel lymph node biopsy sounds minimally invasive, and once the results come back, we can always review and amend the protocol we follow. I just wish to thank each one of you for your devoted support. This could have been a lonely and arduous journey, but I finally feel empowered enough to overcome this mysterious affliction."

From that moment on, we all realized Mom had taken charge of her own destiny, although there was still one piece of the puzzle I wanted to pursue. It had to do with one's thought patterns and how much they influenced a person's well-being. In the book I had just completed reading by Louise Hay called *You Can Heal Your Life*, she states,

"The thoughts we think and the words we speak create our experiences." Perhaps it was prompted by my dream, but there was a part of me that believed Mom, like many people, was struggling with some deep-seated emotions that needed to be unearthed and I was determined to dig them up.

Mom's operation wasn't scheduled until two more weeks, so we all relaxed and enjoyed spending some simple moments together. There was the usual small talk about current affairs, sports or the latest movies we had seen, but nothing compared to the serenity of reminiscing over boxes of old photographs. This communion gave us a chance to appreciate the evolving journey each of us was connected to, and in some mysterious way it seemed much more than simple genetics.

The end of August was fast approaching and I noticed the persistent sun had slowly bleached away the rich green tone of the leaves. I ensured that Mom stuck to her morning and evening ritual of Flor·essence, and each day Willow prepared different concoctions of fresh vegetable juices, along with a fancy array of wholesome meals. Willow and Calin would soon be traveling back home, and shortly after, I was scheduled to follow. Thank God we would still be there to greet Mom after her surgery.

No one ever did claim ownership of the stray golden retriever, so we adopted him as a permanent member of the Young household. With each passing day, he got stronger and stronger, and he brought sparkles of laughter back to the very people who revived his once sullen spirit. One afternoon Dad escorted the trio of Willow, Calin and Lazy Bones on a hike along the river, while I assisted Mom in salvaging the remnants of her summer garden.

"Sometimes life seems strange, son. I'll never comprehend why these perennials have to sit around dormant all winter, and then after finally proliferating into a pageant of beautiful blossoms, they quickly wither away again."

"Perhaps it's all an illusion, Mom. I often think the world we see in front of us is just energy—a palette of vibrating pixels. The more we adhere to the image, the more we struggle with the pixels in our present life. We hold on to problems, we hold on to habits and we hold on to emotions that only we have created. If we free our minds from the things we never really had, we can paint a brand new world."

"I don't understand, dear. Are you saying that we create our own problems? We create our own diseases?"

"I believe we mentally create them, just as I believe we have the power to mentally change them. We begin as open-minded children, and then as we grow through the years, we each learn to react differently to the circumstances we confront. The perceptions and attitudes we develop are conditioned by our surroundings, by our parents and teachers, and by the friends we associate with. Our personal viewpoint might be further reinforced by some fictional character in a book, by the types of television shows and movies we watch, and even the songs and lyrics we listen to. Life is a funny game. Our ideal of reality is constantly solidified through the actions we sustain to preserve a fragile world we so unwarily fabricated. But it is all we have known, so we habitually cling to it long after it has become a boring routine, and yet we are still intimidated by the momentum of the ever-shifting universe around us."

"You wouldn't be hinting at MY life, would you son?"

"I'm referring to all kinds of people. Fear holds so many of us back and it stirs up a whole slough of emotions in the process. I once met a lady who was so afraid of the dark she never ventured out at night. We all know the evening air is harmless, but something triggered her anxiety and she remained imprisoned in her own timid solitude. I believe Granny suffered from her own fears as well. She held on dearly to the past. And guess what part of the body is responsible for letting go of old, decaying energy?"

"The colon? Her colon cancer, of course!"

"Exactly, and I feel there are a lot of similarities between you and Granny. The intimate relationships that fueled you both eventually fell away. First, most of the relatives you loved to entertain moved away. Then Willow and I wandered off to pursue our dreams. And finally, the friendly couriers and local shop owners you loved to fraternize with moved on to more lucrative enterprises. Even Dad became preoccupied with his newly found hobbies. Everyone was busy doing their own thing but you were left feeling empty."

"Maybe there is some truth in that, Vincent. Your dad and I just stayed in this one spot all these years while the community around us underwent a drastic transition. I gradually lost touch with so many things. Gee, I still don't even know how to operate a computer. The older I get, the more I feel like some isolated artifact lost in the junk pile of life."

"We're all getting older, Mom. Just like the petals of these flowers, your once smooth complexion has inherited a few wrinkles and your joints might creak a little more. But this tumor is nothing but some blight on the leaf of your maturing life, and, with the proper replenishment, we will chase it away. No matter how long it takes, no matter what happens, I will always see you as a beautiful flower."

"Oh Vincent, you're giving me goose bumps!"

"That's good Mom! It means your feelings are rising up again." It had been a long time since we shared such a union of hugs and tears, and I knew it was a moment that would forever remain imprinted in our minds. We both sat there for awhile in silence, listening to that deep forgotten place where love whispers its name.

A small flock of swallows swooped by and settled on some nearby telephone lines. The same thing happened two more times before Mom and I stared up to witness a large audience of them nervously shifting about. They mimicked an airport terminal, some taking off into promising skies while others braced themselves for a landing on the narrow strand of wire, claiming the recently vacated spots. Life is a constant ocean of ebbs and flows, cycles of coming and going and seasons of change. At some point, we learn to respect their rhythm and find our own position of balance. Moving back to the familiar faces and moderate pulse of the West Coast was a chance to find mine, and I felt it was time for Mom to find hers.

"Remember when Granny used to give us a quarter to splurge on some candy? It triggered the urge to pursue some sweetness in life, so just like Willow, I enthusiastically ran off for the frills of some foreign city, a new job opportunity or a compelling story. It was stimulating at first, then gradually these temporal pleasures dissolved away like a giant lollipop and I was left feeling unfulfilled. You never did get hooked on some candy syndrome, Mom. You always found a higher source of inspiration and continually brought joy and unconditional love to others. But just like Granny, it often took a toll on your health. We have a tendency to either hold on to the past or yearn for the enticing charms of the future, but we need to be alive in the present. For years you buried your thoughts in hundreds of books, but they are the imaginary dreams of somebody else. You need to discover a gratifying life of your own."

"You are right, Vincent. I went from one extreme to the other. But do you think this has any relevance to my breast cancer?"

I must admit I felt a little awkward tossing the next question at Mom, but it seemed pertinent in uncovering an essential issue regarding her disease. "What does a breast symbolize to you, Mom?"

We both continued pulling up weeds and dead-heading dwindled flower blossoms as she pondered the question. The zealous rays of the sun were streaming down, and I detected her wiping beads of perspiration from her brow before responding. "Hmm, I guess it nurtures life."

"Yes, and you can't nurture life if you are depleted, and you can't nurture life if you are too far removed. You have to pace yourself. Once your health and energy levels are restored, perhaps you can foster your giving spirit by serving as a part-time volunteer. So many people could use a helping hand. I guarantee it will not only bring happiness to others, but it will feed your soul."

"I don't know why I didn't think of that, son. Sometimes we are our own worst enemy. I guess we all struggle within our own mental prison and we just need someone else to point to a path that can free us. Maybe this monster called cancer that feeds on our tissues is really our very own fears and phobias that slowly eat away at us?"

"And I bet they start long before the first few cells behave in an abnormal manner. So many people wrestle with anxiety, depression, loneliness or other negative emotions and they have a powerful impact on our well-being. They vibrate so much faster than any physical substance such as food, drugs or environmental toxins, and the longer we hold onto them, the more they constrict the natural flow of energy in the body and interfere with important life-supporting functions. On the other hand, positive thoughts and emotions can have a profound healing effect. The pure and potent energy of faith, peace, acceptance, joy and love could very well be the medicine of the future."

As Mom and I continued with the gardening, we quietly tried to fathom this new frontier of thinking permeating our consciousness. It was hard to grasp on to something so ethereal, but we both felt we had to follow the guidance of our intuition and explore it further.

It wasn't too long before the rest of the clan came trouncing back from their hike, with Lazy Bones leading the way. Everyone was famished, so we ordered in a generous selection of Thai food and assembled out on the patio. Between mouthfuls, Calin replayed the events of their excursion with the exuberance of a sports announcer. Later on, I took Willow aside and proposed a question that had been simmering away inside of me.

"Have you ever considered relocating back here again, Willow?"

"I'm certainly open to the idea. Calin sure seems to like it here. My husband works in the computer industry—maybe he can find a job in the Seattle area with Microsoft. I'll definitely talk it over with him when we get back. Who knows, after all these years we just might be one big happy family again."

The day suddenly arrived for Mom's operation, and as before, we all piled into the blue Chevy. Instead of heading to the usual clinic, however, we drove to a major hospital in the adjacent town. Dr. Shepherd recommended having the surgery performed there as they were better equipped and had more appropriate rooms where Mom could recover in comfort.

The hospital stood like an ominous monument—a tall rectangle reaching up in prayer to the sacred sky. The outside walls were painted a stark alabaster, but the perimeter was fringed with elegant, ornamental cedars and emerald rhododendrons. Walking up to the entrance, we passed a coral rose garden and a tiered fountain where water cascaded down to a circled arrangement of brightly-colored annuals. The landscaping performed its job admirably, rendering the whole scene quite hospitable, as if tempting one to extend their stay. Inside it was a different story. A frantic front desk was burdened with sobbing victims or casualties wrapped in bloodied bandages. One old man was trembling while pleading for one of the staff to assist him. We thought the decision to come here was a drastic mistake, until we realized we had gone in the Emergency Entrance.

In comparison, the hallway inside the main door was a portrait of serenity, the atmosphere sedated as if on morphine. It felt like we had just disembarked from a time machine and instantly transported from a war zone to a monastery. After checking in, a polite little nurse appeared and casually led Mom away. We were told to come back in around five hours when Mom was likely to be resurfacing from the depths of the anesthesia. This was the part that was out of our control. Soon Mom would be floating in a drug-induced peace while we were left to master our own emotions.

The Journey Home

Appreciate eternity in the moment.

A crescent moon was dangling like a brilliant ivory jewel in the evening sky. Mom was back at home sweet home recuperating in bed while Dad and I were reflecting out on the patio. The night air possessed a slight chill, but it didn't infiltrate the warm thoughts we were sharing.

"I hope that's the worst of it, son," Dad remarked. "Your mom's some special woman and I don't know what I'd do if I ever lost her."

"We can only pray the cancer hasn't spread, but I do have an enormous amount of faith in the regenerating health regime she is sticking to. And to some degree, I trust you will follow it as well. The last thing we need is to go through this whole process again with you somewhere down the road."

"I'll certainly act on your advice. We can never repay you and Willow enough for all the effort and support you have given. Just imagine if you weren't here. With my limited experience, Mom would probably be suffering through painful bouts of chemotherapy or radiation and we'd both be in a real mess."

"So if you were ever diagnosed with prostate cancer, would you let some doctor operate on you?"

"No one is going to fiddle with my precious prostate, son! Not if I can help it." Dad's comment elicited a hearty chuckle from both of us. "Even when you participated in games as a kid, Vincent, you never gave up that easily. Thanks to your persistent research, I'll do anything I can before I blindly submit to some standard procedure. I never realized there is so much accessible information out there nowadays. We live in some pretty amazing times, and one gets the feeling that if one is open-minded just about anything is possible."

"Yes, it seems the important choices each individual makes can be implemented with so much more awareness. I'm currently reading an interesting book titled *Vibrational Medicine* and the author suggests that each soul specifically selects the circumstances of their present incarnation as a vehicle for their own realization and growth. The environments we live in, the relationships we are challenged with and the failures or successes we encounter in the workplace all contribute to the development of our spiritual evolution. The more I ponder over it, the more I believe in the perfect role you and Mom played in my own life. You instilled the discipline I needed to survive in the physical world, while Mom expressed the essence of divine inspiration. In his book, Dr. Richard Gerber also describes inner dimensions of vibrational energy that flows into our gross physical body through a subtle network of energy centers and electrical pathways, and there is a lot of evidence indicating that this energy works in conjunction with various nerve centers, glands and organs. This high-frequency electromagnetic energy can be harnessed through meditation and creative visualization to help balance our emotions and heal disease. In fact, many cancer patients have utilized their intuitive mental powers in these ways to alleviate the personal conflict underlying their own cancer."

"Times sure have changed, son. In the prime of my life, mankind was consumed with acquiring the best paying job, constructing the tallest building or flying to the moon, but maybe they were aiming in the wrong direction."

Dad grew silent and just stared up at the stars, and before too long, I joined him. For the first time, I truly started to appreciate him. I knew he had given up the King of the Castle chase years ago and had resolved to lead a routine existence with Mom. It compelled me to contemplate the thoughts that might hibernate in the subconscious caves of those who grow old. Do they still relish the magical highlights that colored their past, or do they sadly dwell on memories that have long since grayed? How hard is it to cope with a body that is slowly eroding? How confusing is it to witness the manifestations of younger generations who relate to life in a totally different way?

Star gazing always stirred the philosopher within me and after awhile I resumed the conversation. "Life seems like a vast playground filled with an endless array of toys. When we were children, we shared in this blessing, constantly creating colorful games that sustained the sparkle in our eyes. We weren't so concerned about winning or losing, about chasing or being chased, or about amassing the biggest and best assortment of toys. Experiencing fun in the moment was light and magical in itself. As adults, we still participate in a vast playground, but for many of us, the games have become much too serious. We desperately cling to the toys we've worked so hard to accumulate, believing they will bring us security and lifelong happiness. However, instead of experiencing fun in the moment, we play against time. At some point, life will play its game of tag. The Big Bad Wolf will catch us. Ambitious opponents will capture our flag. And the walls of the castle we have built around us will begin to crumble. We worry ourselves into all manner of crippling afflictions. The sparkle in our eyes disappears as we dwell on the future of our fleeting existence. When one identifies with the impermanent objects of the external world, they are bound to experience the unwelcome emotions of regret, sorrow and loss that accompany their inevitable change. It doesn't matter if it's money, employment, possessions or relationships. So many people coil in fear as they approach the vast unknown, especially the dark foreboding serpent called death. But as one gets older it seems the perfect time to embrace the light of our inner soul—that pure and ever peaceful self which remains forever free."

It was getting late and I finally stopped rambling on. I glanced over at Dad and noticed his eyes were closed, his mouth slightly agape and his face still tilted upwards. I wondered if my words had sailed over his head, and in shutting off his mind, he simply fell asleep. Dad must have read my thoughts, for his lips closed and curved into a smile. "I'm still listening. Keep talking, son. Keep talking."

Early next morning, Willow and Calin were up packing their belongings. Their plane flight home was scheduled to depart at 11 a.m. and with having to deal with customs and baggage check-in, we wanted to get them to the airport well in advance. Mom and Dad were busy in the kitchen preparing a farewell breakfast, while I shared a few final words with Willow.

"It's sure been one heck of a month. I really want to thank you, Willow. I couldn't have done it without you."

"Hey, it's family! We always need to be there for each other. Despite the distressing circumstances, Calin and I both had a wonderful time and we learned so much."

"It was pretty enlightening all right, for all of us. This experience opened my eyes to some important things—simple things that are so easy to take for granted."

"Like?"

"Like how fragile life is. How nature is so subtle, yet immensely powerful in its own intricate design. How we need to be vigilant with the kinds of substances we place in our body. How our world can transition with something as simple as a change in our thought patterns or attitude. And of course, how precious our family is, as well as all those close connections that have influenced or inspired our life. They unexpectedly come and go like a passing wind."

"That's so true, Vincent. We can't just find one perfect spot in life and freeze-frame it. Besides, that would be like watching the same movie over and over again. Because circumstances often present an opportunity for change, we need to fully appreciate everything that comes our way."

"So have you given any further thought to what we talked about the other day—about moving back to this area and starting a new phase of your life?"

"You know it would be intriguing to reinvent a fresh model of interior home decorating, perhaps a motif that complements the laid back lifestyle and natural surroundings of the West Coast."

"What do you have in mind?"

"Homes that nurture the soul—huge stone fireplaces for the family to gather around, living spaces that are reflective with tons of comfortable cushions and soft matting for yoga and meditation, an abundance of natural wood and large green plants, sound systems that pipe in serene and relaxing music, ionizers that purify the air, trickling water fountains or salt water aquariums with an array of rainbow fish that silently glide by in their own serene space."

"Fire, wood, earth, water and air—sounds like you wish to incorporate some of the simple elements so prevalent in traditional healing?"

"That's precisely where I came up with the idea, Vincent. In my line of work, I've reinvented basic apartments and I've decorated million-dollar mansions. But despite the size or level of extravagance, the personal dilemmas and dreams of the occupants are no better or worse. They all desire something much deeper and fulfilling. So many people struggle with wanting to improve their station in life, and with wishing to experience a greater level of comfort and joy. Maybe the right conducive environment might stimulate them to look within and appreciate what they have."

"There certainly is a need for people to spend more quality time together, Willow. Sometimes, we can live or work with the same individual for years and hardly ever know them."

Just then we could hear Mom calling us to the kitchen. We all savored the appetizing meal and eagerly watched as Dad presented Calin with a parting gift. The boy's eyes lit up when he unwrapped the present and discovered a small pair of binoculars and a guidebook on bird watching. Calin and Willow were anxious to be heading home, but I knew there was a deep-felt part of them that wanted to stay. Confused stares and whimpers from Lazy Bones as they reluctantly inched out the door didn't help matters.

I wasn't flying out until the next day, so I spent the afternoon reminiscing with Mom and Dad. We also discussed the details regarding my relocating back to Steveston. It was agreed I would temporarily stay in my old bedroom until I found a suitable place of my own. Luckily, the lease on my current apartment was month-to-month, so it would be easy to hand in my termination notice, pack up my sparse collection of belongings and arrange to ship them out west so they could be stored in my parent's basement. If all went according to plan, I would be driving my car back in about three to four weeks.

After supper I grabbed my fleece jacket and decided to stroll into town. I had been so preoccupied that I hardly spent any time outdoors, particularly scrutinizing the setting which would soon become my next home. My starved lungs welcomed the invigorating crisp air as I crisscrossed the grid of streets. Darkness set in early, but a sentry of tall streetlamps illuminated certain sections, tingeing the tops of trees and bathing the walkways with a supernatural glow. A thick fog had rolled in, softening the exterior of the shops, their neon signs straining to remain legible. There were a variety of gift outlets now and chain stores with all too common names; nevertheless, I hadn't yet ventured inside the majority of them. I could have been anywhere—except for the few familiar landmarks stubbornly standing on the same spot they had claimed for generations. Local inhabitants and visitors alike had come to cherish the battered docks, the rustic hotel, the quaint church and even the corner candy store. The town had certainly evolved, but despite modern infringement, nostalgic remnants had been preserved and they evoked a trip down memory lane. My mind was reeling in the good old days when life moved slowly, and I played games in the park or patrolled the ditches for bullfrogs. After all this time, I still felt a special affinity for the place, and perhaps I always would.

I continued on my journey, stopping to admire window displays and people watching. I wondered if any of the clerks or customers could have attended the same school as I had or could have known the same intimate world. Perhaps we were all a new breed now, molded by the uncertain whims of the racing 21st century. On one corner there was a cosy coffee shop, so I decided to duck in from the cold and warm up my blood with a hot drink. Strangers were lounging around, chatting over cappuccinos or tapping away on their laptops, but the server behind the counter looked all too familiar.

"Kenny?"

"You gotta be kidding! Is that you, Vincent?"

"God, it's been at least twenty years! I had no idea you were living back in Steveston."

Kenny rushed out and gave me a huge bear hug. I would have recognized my old skinny friend anywhere. He still wore the same wild garments and fanatical hair style, but his voice imparted a gentle resonance. "Just moved back here six months ago, Vincent. When I'm not toiling away on some fishing vessel, I work here part-time. But what are you up to these days? The last time we spoke you were busy writing articles on women's rights and nuclear arms."

"Oh, I'm still involved in journalism alright. There's no end in sight when it comes to contentious topics to research, but I've actually been out here dealing with family issues. This last month has been one unforgettable experience."

"It sounds like there's a lot to talk about. Let me take your order while you make yourself comfortable. I'll find someone to cover for me and join you shortly." Kenny nodded toward a table in the corner and disappeared into the back. A few minutes later, he was sitting across from me with two big ceramic mugs of hot chocolate, steam swirling in front of his lingering dazed expression. "I still can't believe my eyes, Vincent. How long are you going to be in town for?"

"Unfortunately, I'm going to be flying home to Toronto tomorrow, but the good news is that I'll be moving back here permanently." I filled Kenny in with a brief description of the various cities I had lived in and some of the top stories that marked my professional career. I couldn't wait to hear what kinds of mischief Kenny had encountered over the years. "So apart from working on fishing boats, what else have you been involved in?"

Kenny took a gulp of his cocoa and recalled snippets from his gallivanting ways. "I was a lifeguard at Kitsilano Beach for about five years and then banged drums and sang backup in a local rock band. When my tonsils and hearing started waning, I shifted to supervising blueberry pickers at a farm in Richmond. The pay wasn't very good, so I eventually moved into something that really intrigued me."

"What was that? I asked.

"I took courses on massage and other healing arts and became a holistic practitioner."

"That's wonderful!" I stressed. "I always thought you would have a knack for something aesthetic and ethereal like that. It seems to be compatible with your unconventional nature. So what happened? Why did you give it up?"

"I did have a natural talent for it, Vincent, but you know me—always seeking new experiences, each experience as rewarding as the next until the magic wears off and it becomes a routine."

"So I traveled all over the continent and all I did was write, while you lived within a stone's throw of here and experienced a rich tapestry of colorful pursuits. It makes you wonder, doesn't it?"

"I've always found life as incredible as it is unpredictable, my friend. You're finally ready to settle down and you meet up with a bouncing ball like me again."

"Yeah, why do I get this incredulous feeling that life back in Steveston will never be boring?"

"I promise I'll do my best to keep you on your toes, Vincent." While we were chatting, Kenny was fidgeting with this glass shaker of sugar on the table and managed to balance it on one edge at a 45-degree angle. It appeared to be an illusion, but I had seen the trick done before and realized it was simply a matter of physics. Kenny just kept on talking with this stoic expression, as if nothing had happened. "You mentioned you were out here because of family issues. Is it something serious?"

I relayed the news about Mom's illness and how we all pooled our efforts together to explore the most viable treatment options. Kenny conveyed his regards and was more than anxious to offer his assistance. "Maybe I can do some healing work on your mom one of these days. Free of charge, of course."

"I appreciate that, Kenny. Every little bit helps."

"You know, during my stint as a massage therapist, I participated in numerous holistic workshops and met some extraordinary practitioners. Everyone seemed to possess a genuine interest in personal transformation and their specialized treatment always transcended the patient's symptom. Come to think of it, I once visited this complementary cancer care facility up in Vancouver. Their goal is to empower people to look beyond their illness and discover a broader and more inspired approach to reestablishing their health. They're actually funded by the government and have both conventional and naturopathic physicians on staff. They offer life enhancing seminars on nutrition, cooking, exercise and meditation, as well as emotional support and spiritual guidance."

"It sounds like they really integrate a whole person model of healing. What's the name of this place, Kenny?"

"You hit the nail on the head, Vincent. It's called the Centre for Integrated Healing.* I don't mind taking your mom there sometime. She can at least go on the free introductory tour and browse through their extensive library."

I was impressed with Kenny's wealth of information. He had to get back to work, so we exchanged farewells and made a promise to spend some time together in the future. I downed the last ounce of warm cocoa and stepped out into the fog.

The next day Mom and Dad dropped me off at the airport. They were sad to see me leaving, but somewhat excited knowing that I would soon be returning. I handed Mom Kenny's phone number and indicated I would be calling her on a regular basis to check on her progress. Sailing into the calm blue skies infused my mind with optimism.

Back at my apartment, I focused my energy on packing

*At press time the name of the center had been changed to Inspire Health.

and finishing a few articles I had been working on. Being in a bustling metropolis again was a shock to my system, and I actually looked forward to the distraction of tying up a cluster of loose ends. I phoned Mom, as promised, and with each passing week was glad to hear that her condition kept improving. When the results from the sentinel lymph node biopsy came back, we were all relieved to learn that the tumor had not spread. Whether it was the Flor·essence, the improved diet or her revived spirit, I'll never know. And it seems that Dr. Shepherd was overcome with as much joy as anyone in the family. The battle against a sly enemy was over, but Mom's commitment to maintaining a healthy lifestyle never ceased. She booked a massage session with Kenny and described the experience as heavenly. During another telephone conversation, she elaborated on the informative tour at the Centre for Integrated Healing. Mom was so inspired she even attended some of the seminars, and was fortunate to have met some volunteers who encouraged her to help out at a local cancer clinic. The fulfillment of helping others find a brighter life could now be realized.

As for me, the emotional ordeal of the past few months could be left behind. I welcomed the cross-country drive that presented a perfect opportunity for reflection. Passing through the forested hills and lakes of northern Ontario, the endless miles of golden prairie and the majestic snow-capped peaks of the Rockies awakened my awareness for the grandeur and diversity of mother earth. We didn't have to change the planet, only how we lived our lives. So many people become preoccupied in their own lost world, often forgetting the beauty that surrounds them. God had certainly created an abundant playground, but the only thing lacking, the one contribution with boundless potential, was human kindness. Like Mom, this was the loving ember I needed to kindle, the often neglected virtue I needed most to write about. There were good Samaritans hidden in all walks of life, quietly serving in every community. After I completed my journey home, I made a vow to find them and share their stories.

Christmas Eve arrived and a rare snow carpeted the little town of Steveston in a glittering white. Presents were piled high under the tree, but the real gift was having the whole family together again. Calin, Willow and her husband were visiting for the holidays and announced they would be moving to the West Coast in the coming year. After a celebration of food, games and laughter, we all sat back and counted our blessings. Mom brought out the eggnog and made a toast to everyone's health, including Lazy Bones, who was curled up beside Calin and never seemed happier.

Unlike some folks, it was our tradition to open the presents at midnight, so we passed the time watching our favorite Yuletide classics. They never ceased to ruffle my heart strings and I couldn't resist pulling Mom aside.

"Do you ever consider why so many people embrace movies like A CHRISTMAS CAROL and IT'S A WONDERFUL LIFE?"

"Why dear?"

"Perhaps we identify with being in a place of despair and rising to a reverence for life. At some point along our path, at some bend in the road, an event will most likely trigger a challenge that is similar. I remember you once said that the weary are often blessed with a guiding presence. For some lost souls a dreamlike apparition or angelic friend just might shed a light on their troubles. When we least expect it, God graciously grants us a gift to wake us up. In a strange way, your confrontation with cancer is like a gift—a calling presenting an opportunity to resurrect your life."

"I never thought of it in that way, son. It seems these past few months have been a real eye opener for all of us. I not only feel so much healthier, but am inspired with a renewed purpose. Helping out as a volunteer has made me realize there is so much more I can offer then simply devoting all of my energy toward our family. So many people don't have the luxury of loving support. Most of the cancer patients I work with just want another compassionate being to talk to."

"Well, I can't think of a more suitable person for the job, Mom. I'm proud of you, we're all proud of you, for reaching out to others. It takes a mountain of courage to endure what you've gone through and still give of yourself so selflessly. That's what the true spirit of Christmas is all about."

Although it was frigid outside, this special warmth permeated the living room of our parent's household. And it wasn't just the crackling logs in the fireplace, the lights twinkling on the tree or the soothing holiday carols seeping from the stereo. It was something much grander. When life steals away something precious, and then in its own mystical way brings it all back again, it humbles the skeptic within and fuels the faith of all involved. Cancer can be beaten. That which is broken can be healed. Fragmented families can be reunited. Perhaps in some not so distant time, tradition will respectfully merge with technology, divided nations will peacefully share the earth, and the past and the future will melt into the present. For the moment, I was a child enchanted with the innocent festivities of a family. All was alive and well in my tiny universe once again.

Appendix

TEN STEPS FOR OVERCOMING CANCER

Currently, the most prominent types of cancer expected to occur in American men are associated with the prostate, lung/bronchus, colon/rectum and urinary system. In American women, the most commonly diagnosed types of cancer are cancers of the breast, lung/bronchus, colon/rectum and genital system (uterus/ovaries). Leading cancer deaths for both genders are lung related, affecting one in three males (approximately 31%) and one in four females (approximately 26%). In fact, the American Cancer Society estimates around 170,000 annual cancer deaths will occur due to tobacco use alone.

Fortunately, the majority of cancers today are now being attributed to unhealthy lifestyle factors within our control. Poor dietary habits, lack of sufficient exercise, tobacco and alcohol abuse, as well as emotional stress can all be addressed by each individual. Consider the following guidelines as a tool for preventing cancer or helping to overcome an existing condition:

REGULAR MEDICAL CHECKUPS – don't wait until it is too late or the pain becomes unbearable before seeing your doctor. Regular checkups and screening examinations by your health practitioner can detect various cancers in their early stages. Studies indicate the recent decline in breast and prostate cancer mortality are the result of early detection and the increased treatment options. If you are diagnosed with cancer, always obtain a second opinion and carefully choose the medical facility and health care professional managing your treatment.

PERSONAL RESEARCH – there is no need to walk blindly when confronted with cancer or any other serious disease. An abundance of educational information is available at the local library, bookstore and on the Internet. Cancer facts, conventional treatments, personal stories, research data and holistic approaches to dealing with cancer are readily accessible and will help you in making a clearer decision regarding your available options.

ELIMINATION OF TOXINS – thousands of chemical preservatives, synthetic additives, pesticide residues, hormones and other harmful substances contaminate our food, water and air supply. Their combined and cumulative effect can have a detrimental impact on the state of our health. Many natural food outlets and supermarkets stock produce and other foodstuffs which are organic or unadulterated. There is also numerous personal body care and home living products available that are safer for your family and the environment. And appliances such as water purifiers, air filters/ionizers and anti-radiation devices for computers and cell phones can also enhance modern day living (see Health References).

HEALTHY FLUID INTAKE – elimination or reduction in alcohol, caffeine and soda pop or beverages saturated with refined sugar or high fructose corn syrup can go a long way in improving your overall health. Studies link alcohol consumption with higher incidences of colorectal cancer. Drinking at least two liters of purified water daily is beneficial for flushing out undesirable toxins from the body. Green tea is rich in antioxidants and catechins that strengthen the immune system and fresh-pressed vegetable and fruit juices provide concentrated nutrients, enzymes and fiber that support digestion and help repair damaged cells.

WHOLESOME DIETING – a diet with a high percentage of fresh, organic fruits and vegetables and whole grains offers a plethora of vitamins, minerals, phytochemicals and fiber that provide amazing healing benefits (see Diet Recommendations). Reducing caloric intake by eating less and avoiding snack foods laden with sugar and refined carbohydrates can help maintain ideal weight and prevent obesity, which has a correlation with increased cancer risk as well as cardiovascular disease. Eliminating excess saturated fats, as occurring in meat and dairy products, may reduce common cancers such as breast, prostate and colon. Replacing refined, hydrogenated oils with fresh-pressed, unrefined healthy oils will provide valuable essential fatty acids that are necessary for a variety of key bodily functions.

INTERNAL CLEANSING – a weakened state of health often coincides with an accumulation of toxins that compromise the body's inherent ability to function effectively. Faltering digestion, elimination, immune response and sluggish energy are signals of tissue imbalance. A patient and methodical cleansing regime is one of the most important commitments one can make on the road to recovery and a return to rejuvenated health. Forcing toxins from the body by rigorous fasting or removing accumulated wastes with aggressive cleansing kits that irritate the colon and unleash a floodgate of uncomfortable side-effects is not recommended. Once the body has achieved an optimum state of health one can experiment with other cleansing programs, but Flor·essence offers a gentle and safe means of purification that reestablishes the body's natural balance and that is why I have given it so much focus. The herbs in Flor·essence remarkably identify, gather together and flush away toxic residue from congested cells, organs and bloodstream. Its antioxidant properties also neutralize free radicals that lead to abnormal cell damage.

ADDITIONAL SUPPLEMENTS – one can easily go overboard taking scores of vitamins, minerals, herbs and other nutritional formulas, but they should never replace the foundation of a wholesome, nourishing diet and healthy lifestyle. Complementing your therapeutic program with a strategic selection of quality supplements however, may add a positive contribution to cancer prevention or cancer recovery therapy.

Holistic doctors, naturopaths and health store assistants can offer guidance regarding reputable brands and key products prepared with quality ingredients and supported by science or research. Some choice supplements include: a complete multivitamin formula in a natural base to counteract nutrient deficiencies; full-spectrum plant enzymes to assist digestion; probiotics comprised of human-based strains of *Lactobacillus acidophilus* and *Lactobacillus bifidus* which have been successfully tested for their gastric resistance and ability to implant in the intestinal tract (a minimum of 2 billion live microorganisms per capsule); antioxidants for immune enhancement including vitamins A, C and E, beta-carotene, the minerals selenium and zinc, coenzyme Q-10 and grape seed extract (standardized for proanthocyanidin content); milk thistle for stimulating liver function; and pure, filler-free wheatgrass or barley grass juice powders which provide energy, help restore body pH and mitigate the damaging effects of free radicals. Numerous studies have been conducted on medicinal mushrooms such a maitake, shiitake and reishi, indicating their anti-inflammatory and tumor inhibiting properties. Research on D-Fraction, a beta glucan extract from maitake mushrooms, demonstrated its ability to not only inhibit carcinogenesis and metastasis, but act synergistically with certain chemotherapy drugs (see Health References).

ADEQUATE EXERCISE – moderate to vigorous physical activity of at least 30 minutes per day may reduce the risk of colon, breast and other cancers, as well as help maintain a healthy body weight. Sufficient exercise will also improve appetite, digestion, blood sugar imbalance, circulation, muscle tone and energy levels. Brisk walks, jogging or hiking in an outdoor, clean air environment delivers life sustaining oxygen to the lungs, bloodstream and cells.

STRESS REDUCTION – many of the nagging thoughts that persistently plague our mental well-being are self-induced. How we see the world and the way we react to it is unique to each individual. One person might be totally at ease in a particular setting or situation that another person finds distressful or even terrifying. Our life experience is ours to master. Helen Schucman, scribe for *A Course In Miracles* states "On the path to knowledge, many thoughts are accumulated. On the path to wisdom, many thoughts are discarded". Sitting in quiet meditation on a regular basis is an ideal way of calming the mental noise that often taints our existence with worry and discontentment. Peace and mental clarity can also be attained through practicing yoga, tai chi, visualization and deep breathing, or simply engaging in nurturing activities like gardening or playing a soothing musical instrument.

LOVING SUPPORT – Disease (dis-ease) comes from separation, while healing comes from wholeness. Feelings of loneliness, isolation, self-pity and self-doubt become more common as we age, especially if we are confronted with cancer or some debilitating condition. We need to open up our arms to those family members and friends who are usually more than anxious to reach out to us. We have to reestablish our connection with the life around us. Participating in family gatherings, sharing in activities with friends, joining a support group or even becoming a volunteer in the community, reinforces our sense of place in a world where people care. Love is a magical gift that makes everyone feel like they belong.

DIET RECOMMENDATIONS

A well-balanced and nourishing diet rich in natural healing components is extremely helpful in preventing or reversing cancer. High vibrational foods have many purifying, life-enhancing qualities and a sufficient intake of them will contribute to optimum health. They are easier to digest, mucus free and primarily alkaline forming. Their cooling (yin) properties are also beneficial for easing the inflammation and irritation that accompanies most diseases. On the other hand, low vibrational foods are more difficult to digest. Their mucus forming, acidic and heat inducing (yang) nature contribute to congestion and inflammation if consumed in excess.

HIGH VIBRATION FOODS	LOW VIBRATION FOODS
pure/filtered water	soda pop, alcohol
herbal teas (especially green tea)	coffee
fresh-pressed fruit & vegetable juices	pasteurized juices
raw fruits & vegetables	canned fruits & vegetables
leafy greens, sprouts	potatoes (esp. french fries)
raw nuts & seeds (esp. flax seeds	red meat, fowl
whole grains (wild rice, brown rice	pasta, white rice,
millet, quinoa, amaranth and spelt)	white bread, baked desserts
live-cultured yogurt	dairy (milk, butter, cheese,
wheatgrass/barley grass juice, spirulina, chlorella	eggs, ice-cream)
bee pollen	packaged junk food

HELPFUL HINTS

- Drink plenty of pure water (2 or more liters daily) to rinse cells and flush out toxic wastes.
- Incorporate invigorating health shakes that combine protein and/or cereal grass powder with juice, yogurt, enzymes, liquid aloe vera, flax oil or a flax oil blend and fresh or frozen berries.
- Chew food sufficiently to enhance digestion.
- Consume more small meals instead of a few large meals throughout the day.
- Follow basic food combining principals as much as possible (proteins combine well with vegetables, starches combine well with vegetables, proteins and starches do not mix well nor do fruits and vegetables).
- Balance caloric intake with level of physical activity to maintain a healthy weight.
- Get adequate amounts of rest and sound sleep.

Thought Vibrations

Just like the physical body, the mental body has thought patterns that can be life enhancing or life depleting. Emotions elicit powerful vibrational frequencies and continually holding on to negative thoughts can block the energy that fuels various parts of the body. A sound diet of positive emotions can have a profound impact on our well-being. For instance, if you are consistently feeling depressed (lungs), then create and meditate on an affirmation that is resurrecting— *I am cheerful and truly appreciate being alive.* Find the emotions in the following chart that best relate to you.

Negative Emotions	Positive Emotions	Relationship to Body
Indecisive	Decisive	Brain
Agitated	Peaceful	Nervous system
Stifled	Expressive	Throat
Depressed	Cheerful	Lungs
Unloved, Insecure	Loved, Secure	Heart
Impatient, Repulsive	Patient, Acceptable	Stomach
Distressed	Content	Liver
Proud	Humble	Gall Bladder
Repressed	Freedom	Adrenals
Intolerant	Understanding	Kidneys
Futile, Weary	Hopeful, Refreshed	Urinary/Bladder
Rejected	Approved	Pancreas
Selfish	Unselfish	Small Intestines
Cut off, Constricted	United, Clear	Large Intestines
Unfruitful, Unproductive	Fruitful, Productive	Reproductive
Uneasy, Scared	Harmonious, Courageous	Skin

Profile of Flor-Essence

FLOR·ESSENCE USAGE

The amount of Flor·essence any given individual can take is different, depending on the age, size and level of health involved. It is important to remember that each person is responsible for his or her own healing. Try to distinguish what your various signs and symptoms mean, and how to change negative signs into positive ones with wholesome foods, healthy beverages and rejuvenating remedies.

When not preparing Flor·essence, the herbal tea should be kept refrigerated at all times. Shake well before each use and always dilute each serving with an equal or double amount of purified hot or cold water. Ideally, Flo·ressence should be consumed on an empty stomach before bedtime and one hour before breakfast. Sip slowly and wait at least an hour before eating or drinking other foodstuff.

The amount of Flor·essence needs to be adjusted, depending on the goal and the severity of the symptoms. It is recommended to start at the maintenance dose and increase gradually to minimize healing reactions, such as nausea, headaches or diarrhea. Since Flor·essence cleanses the body of toxins, its use is not recommended for pregnant or nursing women.

ADULTS
Daily maintenance: Measure out 1 to 2 oz. of tea and take twice daily.

Cleansing and detoxification: Measure out 2 oz. of tea and take twice daily for 24 to 48 days. Repeat as necessary.

Active illness: Measure out 3 oz. of tea and take twice daily.

CHILDREN (2 to 12 years of age)
Daily maintenance or cleansing: Measure out 1 oz. of tea and take once a day, either early morning or before bedtime.

Active illness: Measure out 1 oz. of tea and take twice daily.

INFANTS (under 2 years of age)

Daily maintenance or cleansing: Measure out ½ oz. of tea and take once a day, either early morning or before bedtime.

Active illness: Measure out ½ oz of tea and take twice daily.

PETS

For an active illness, give every day on an empty stomach. If there is a strong resistance on the part of your pet, pour the tea on their food. When the symptoms are corrected, adjust to a maintenance program of 3 X weekly and continue until proof of healing.

Weight	Flor·essence	Weight	Flor·essence
1-5 lbs	1-1½ tbsp	31-60 lbs	2-3 ozs
6-15 lbs	1 oz (2 tbsp)	61- 120 lbs	3-4 ozs
16-30 lbs	1-2 ozs	over 120 lb	4-6 ozs

The Healing Benefits of Flor·Essence

Flor·essence is highly regarded throughout the world as a gentle yet powerful herbal formula for detoxification, immune support and improved digestive function. Its unique capacity for rejuvenating cells is ideal for reversing a wide variety of serious health conditions and restoring people of all ages with renewed vitality. Flor·essence is carefully prepared with aqueous extracts of herbs, which makes it safe when taken as directed. Although the synergistic action of the eight herbs gives Flor·essence superior healing advantages over its individual components, it is helpful to understand the mechanism behind each one.

Burdock root
Scientific name: *Arctium lappa L.*

Active ingredients: Burdock root contains from 27-45% inulin, mucilage, essential oils, antioxidant rich flavonoids and polyphenols, antibacterial polyacetylenes, bitter substances, beta-sitosterol, vitamins, trace minerals and protein.

Healing properties: Burdock has been traditionally used in Europe and Asia to purify the blood, help ease respiratory disorders, stimulate the excretion of urine (diuretic) and treat skin blemishes. Inulin, one of the key components of burdock root, is part of the complex carbohydrate known as fructo-oligo-saccharides, which help increase intestinal flora and balance blood sugar. The tea made from burdock root reduces inflammation and supports the cleansing and toning of the liver, gall bladder, kidneys and colon. Various studies have also indicated the value of burdock in preventing or reducing cell mutation. Other benefits include the use of burdock for joint pain, hair loss, as a gentle laxative and as an anti-microbial agent.

Research references:

Lin CC, Lu JM, Yang JJ, et al. Anti-inflammatory and radical scavenge effects of Arctium lappa. Am J Chin Med 1996; 24:127-137

Morita K, Kada T, Namiki M. A desmutagenic factor isolated from burdock (Arctium lappa Linne). Mutation Res 1984; 129:25-31

Sheep sorrel

Scientific name: *Rumex acetosella L.*

Active ingredients: Sheep sorrel contains a wide spectrum of nutrients including vitamin A, B complex, vitamin C, D, E, K, P and U, as well as valuable minerals such as calcium, potassium, magnesium, phosphorus, silicon, sodium, iron, copper, sulphur, iodine, manganese and zinc. The leaves and stems provide a rich supply of chlorophyll, carotenoids and organic acids. Anthraquinones, such as emodin, aloe-emodin, rhein and chrysophanol are also present.

Healing properties: Sheep sorrel has traditionally been used as a diuretic, laxative, astringent and anti-inflammatory. Its popularity has thrived among various Native tribes throughout North America as a food and as a medicinal treatment for fevers, stomach ulcerations and cancer. The high chlorophyll content is excellent for oxygenating the tissues, cleansing the blood and inhibiting the growth of bacteria and other pathogens. In the 1930's, Dr. Otto Warburg received the Nobel Prize for discovering that a lack of oxygen in the tissues triggers cell mutation. The chlorophyll in sheep sorrel is vital for increasing the oxygen content of the blood and thwarting the growth of cancer. The carotenoids and anthraquinones in the plant provide antioxidant support, which prevent cell damage due to harmful free radicals, however excessive amounts of anthraquinones may exert a laxative effect. Raw sheep sorrel leaves are sometimes added as a salad green, but should be used sparingly as they have a high oxalic acid and tannin content (the aqueous extracts of sheep sorrel as found in Flor·essence contain only trace amounts).

Research references:

Fairbairn JW, and Muhtadi FJ. Chemotaxonomy of Anthraquinones in Rumex. Phytochemistry 1972; 11:263-268

Hutchens A. *Indian Herbalogy of North America.* Shambhala Publications. Boston, Mass: 1991: 255-256

TURKISH RHUBARB ROOT
Scientific name: *Rheum palmatum L.*

Active ingredients: Turkish rhubarb root contains vitamins and minerals, several anthraquinones (3-12%) such as chrysophanol, emodin, aloe-emodin and rhein, as well as dianthraquinones (10-25%), plant resins, tannins, bioflavonoids (including rutin) and polyphenols.

Healing properties: Turkish rhubarb root has been used traditionally to enhance digestion, stimulate loss of appetite and normalize bowel function. Depending on the applied dosage, it can alleviate both diarrhea and constipation. The German Pharmacopoeia recommends rhubarb root for constipation and related disorders. The tannins present in Turkish rhubarb root stimulate gastric secretions and improve the functioning of the liver, gall bladder and stomach. Emodin possesses anti-inflammatory, antispasmodic and anti-ulcer properties (reduces bleeding in the upper digestive tract). The herb also helps purge the body of harmful parasites and toxic wastes. In fact, rhein inhibits the growth of pathogens in the intestinal tract, including Candida albicans.

Research references:

Driscoll JS, Hazard JrHB, Wood Jr, and Goldin A. Structure-anti-tumor activity relationships among quinine derivatives. Cancer Chem Rep 1974; Part 2 4:1-27

Yagi T, Yamauchi K, and Kuwano S. The synergistic purgative action of aloe-emodin anthrone and rhein anthrone in mice: synergism in large intestinal propulsion and water secretion. J Pharm Pharmacol 1997; 49:22-25

SLIPPERY ELM BARK

Scientific name: *Ulmus rubra Muhl, Ulmus fulva Muhl*

Active ingredients: Slippery elm bark contains a complex combination of polysaccharides (mucilage), vitamins, minerals, carbohydrates, gallic acid, galactose, carbolic acid, antioxidants (including beta-sitosterol) and flavonoids.

Healing properties: Slippery elm bark has been popular in both North America and Asia as a traditional healing remedy. For centuries Native Americans have utilized poultices made from the mucilage of slippery elm bark for treating infected wounds, burns and abrasions of the skin. This sticky, mucilaginous fiber is extremely effective for soothing inflammation of the mucous membranes lining the throat and entire digestive tract, including the stomach, kidneys and intestines. Its adhesive and lubricating qualities allows for toxic waste material to be gathered up and eliminated from the body. Along with its antioxidant properties, slippery elm has merit in treating ulcers and irritated bowel tissue. The gallic acid present in slippery elm has anti-fungal and anti-viral properties and exhibits cytotoxic action against cancer, without harming healthy cells.

Research references:

Bock S. Integrative medical treatment of inflammatory bowel disease. Int J Integr Med 2000; 2(5):21-29

Hutchens A. *Indian Herbalogy of North America.* Shambhala Publications. Boston, Mass: 1991: 252-253
Langmead L, Dawson C, Hawkins C, Banna N, Loo S, Rampton DS. Antioxidant effects of herbal therapies used by patients with inflammatory bowel disease: an in vitro study. Ailment Pharmacol Ther 2002; 16(2):197-205

Tierra M. *The Way of Herbs.* Pocket Books. New York, NY:1998: 194-195

WATERCRESS

Scientific name: *Nasturtium officinale R. Br.*

Active ingredients: Watercress is rich in nutrients, especially vitamins A, B, C and E, the minerals calcium, magnesium, potassium, phosphorus, and iodine, as well as amino acids and chlorophyll. The fresh plant also contains mustard oil glycosides (glucosinolates), specifically gluconasturtiin.

Healing properties: Watercress was traditionally used as a remedy for kidney and liver problems, lethargy, rheumatism, scurvy and purifying the blood. It is a general stimulant for the digestive organs strengthens immune response. Compounds in watercress (specifically gluconasturtiin) have cytotoxic activity and are known to activate detoxification enzymes in abnormal cells, which help reduce their growth. Other compounds in watercress benefit the lungs and bronchial tract and are now being recognized for their role in preventing lung disease in smokers.

Research references:

Hecht SS, Chung FL, Richie JPJr, Akerkar SA, Borukhova A, Skowronski L, and Carmella SG. Effects of watercress consumption on metabolism of a tobacco-specific lung carcinogen in smokers. Cancer Epidemiol Biomarkers 1995; Prev 4 (8):877-884

KELP

Scientific name: *Laminaria digitata*

Active ingredients: Kelp is abundant in minerals and trace elements, particularly iodine, calcium, magnesium, potassium, sodium, phosphorus, iron and silicon. Vitamin A, C and E, and some B vitamins are also present, as are fatty acids, amino acids, carbohydrates, fiber and alginates.

Healing properties: This brown, edible seaweed provides an excellent source of iodine, which regulates the thyroid gland and has an impact on cellular metabolism, immune response and weight loss or gain. Kelp also re-mineralizes the body, eliminates toxins from the intestines and deters abnormal cell growth. The alginates in kelp stimulate and soothe digestion and prevent the absorption of toxic metals, including radioactive Strontium 90, a by-product of nuclear power and weapons facilities. Studies indicate that alginate supplements can reduce Strontium 90 absorption by up to 83%.

Research references:

Sutton A, Harrison GE, Carr TEF, and Barltrop D. Reduction in the absorption of dietary strontium in children by an alginate derivative. Int J Radiat Biol 1971; 19 (1):79-85

Yamamoto I, Nagumo T, Yagi K, Tominaga H, and Aoki M. Anti-tumor effects of seaweeds. 1. Anti-tumor effects of extracts from sargassum and laminaria. Jpn J Exp Med 1974; 44 (6):543-546

BLESSED THISTLE
Scientific name: *Cnicus benedictus L.*

Active ingredients: Blessed thistle is composed of bitter substances, including cnicin (a sesquiterpenoid lactone), mucilage, flavonoids, lignans, minerals, phytosterols and essential oil.

Healing properties: Blessed thistle is commonly used for liver congestion and other digestive disorders. Through its bitter properties, the herb is known to increase the flow of gastric juices and bile acid secretions, thus relieving dyspepsia, stimulating the appetite and cleansing the kidneys and liver. It not only strengthens the body and rejuvenates cells, but is also effective for treating internal bleeding, headache, fever and joint pain. Research has demonstrated that the bitter principals and other active substances found in blessed thistle have anti-bacterial and antiviral activity.

Research references:

Rodriguez E, Towers GHN, and Mitchell JC. Biological activities of sesquiterpene lactones. Phytochemistry 1976; 15:1573-1580

Tierra M. *The Way of Herbs.* Pocket Books. New York, NY:1998: 97-98

Vanhaelen-Fastre R, and Vanhaelen M. Antibiotic and cytotoxic activity of cnicin and of its hydrolysis products. Chemical structure – biological activity relationship. Planta Med 1976; 29 (2):179-189

RED CLOVER
Scientific name: *Trifolium pretense L.*

Active ingredients: Red clover contains antioxidant rich flavonoids, isoflavones, tannins, glycosides, coumarins, vitamins, minerals and phytoestrogens (genistein, daidzein, formononetin and biochanin-A).

Healing properties: Traditionally, red clover has been used by numerous cultures throughout the world to treat cancer and various tumors, as well as infections, respiratory problems, nervous disorders and inflamed skin conditions. It is also an excellent detoxifier and blood purifier, facilitating the removal of toxic wastes from the body tissues. Dr. Jonathan Hartwell of the National Cancer Institute (NCI) discovered four separate anti-tumor compounds in red clover. And the phytoestrogens present in red clover are now recognized for their anti-estrogenic benefits. Studies with phytoestrogens indicate they not only counteract the potential side-effects of Hormone Replacement Therapy drugs, but help maintain proper bone density and relieve hot flashes and night sweats. They also inhibit abnormal cell growth in both men and women.

Research references:

Hutchens A. *Indian Herbalogy of North America.* Shambhala Publications. Boston, Mass:1991: 233-234

Stephens FO. Phytoestrogens and prostate cancer: possible preventive role. Med J Aust 1997; 167 (3):138-140

Tierra M. *The Way of Herbs.* Pocket Books, New York, NY: 1998: 185

Flow Chart of Disease Progression

Developed by Bev Maya, Medical Herbalist

The following 2 charts have been compiled by Bev Maya (visit her web site at www. mayanaturalhealth.com) to illustrate the typical stages of disease progression in an individual and how Flor·essence helps to reverse this process. The benefits listed here pertain only to the model shown and it is important to remember that the herbs in Flor·essence have numerous other healing properties as well.

Disease Development	Description	Symptoms
Toxins	gradual buildup of toxins from food, stress and environmental chemicals in the air and water	initiation of subtle health changes
pH Disruption	toxic overload creates an acid/alkaline imbalance resulting in impaired digestion	gastritis, ulcers, heartburn, stone formation(ie. kidney stones, gallstones), poor or malabsorption of food
Inflammation & Congestion	accumulation of acids and other wastes irritate tissues causing congestion and swelling	all the 'itis' conditions (ie. arthritis), migraine, asthma, high blood pressure
Increased Mucous Membrane Permeability	membranes become porous (leaky gut syndrome) allowing toxins and undigested matter to re-circulate	fluid imbalances, bloating, bowel changes
Invasion of Toxins	accelerated invasion of toxins with side-effects due to further digestive disruption	worsened digestion, mood swings, insomnia, allergies
Immuno-endocrine Dysfunction	suppressed immune function and hormonal imbalance contribute to onset of auto-immune conditions	Crohn's disease, multiple sclerosis, diabetes, hyper or hypo endocrine function
Increased DNA Mutation	proliferation of abnormal cells which congregate in colonies	cervical dysplasia, benign growths
Apoptosis Dysfunction	damaged cells respond to signals triggering programmed cell death	serious cellular change and destruction

FLOR·ESSENCE REVERSES THE DISEASE PROCESS

ACTION	FLOR·ESSENCE HERBS INVOLVED	DESCRIPTION
Alleviate toxins	burdock root, slippery elm, blessed thistle, watercress	burdock and watercress are excellent blood purifiers, blessed thistle increases gland secretion encouraging eliminination of toxins
Re-establish pH balance	slippery elm	balances pH and soothes irritated membranes
Decrease membrane permeability	slippery elm, red clover turkish rhubarb	slippery elm and turkish rhubarb tighten and protect membranes
Flood body with nutrients and antioxidants	sheep sorrel, watercress, turkish rhubarb, red clover	sheep sorrel and watercress are rich in minerals and antioxidants (chlorophyll and vitamins A, C and E)
Maximize elimination pathways	turkish rhubarb, sheep sorrel, blessed thistle	turkish rhubarb increases peristalsis, sheep sorrel and blessed thistle stimulates gastric juices
Re-set immune function	kelp	kelp balances immune system and protects against radiation
Emphasize parasympathetic nervous system activity	red clover	red clover relaxes the nervous system
Increase tissue perfusion	sheep sorrel, burdock root, kelp, turkish rhubarb	sheep sorrel provides oxygen to tissue at the cellular level, burdock root relaxes muscles around organs
Decrease cell destruction	burdock root	burdock root decreases mutations in cells damaged toxic overload

FLOR·ESSENCE® HERBAL TONIC USE IN NORTH AMERICA:
A Profile of General Consumers and Cancer Patients

HerbalGram
The Journal of the American Botanical Council
Issue: 50 Page: 40-46

by Mary Ann Richardson, DrPH*, Tina Sanders, MPH*,
Carmen Tamayo, MD+, Carrie Perez, MPH*, J. Lynn Palmer, PhD**

*   Centers for Alternative Medicine Research and Health Promotion
    Research and Development, The University of Texas-Houston
    School of Public Health

+   Foresight Link Corporation, Ontario, Canada

** Department of Biostatistics, The University of Texas M.D. Anderson
    Cancer Center

ABSTRACT

Objectives: Flor-Essence® and Essiac™ are widely used herbal tonics. After three decades, little is known about consumers using them. This pattern-of-use survey was conducted to 1) profile consumers, 2) characterize cancer patients, and 3) determine reasons for use, benefits, and adverse events.

Methods: A population-based study assessed Flor-Essence consumers in North America between June 1998 and August 1999. Data are presented in frequencies and proportions.

Results: Of 5,051 consumers (response 6.4%), most were Caucasian, educated, American, long-term users (mean 15.8 months, SD=17.4), and cancer patients. Of 1,577 cancer patients (response 42.4%), 85.3% were treated previously and 36.8% currently with conventional medicine for breast, prostate, or lung cancer. Overall, 64.5% discussed using the tonic with physicians; few (11.4%) exceeded the recommended dose. Most patients (50.6%) reported improvement in symptoms, but 6.6% experienced adverse events.

Conclusions: The tonic is widely distributed. Many cancer patients combine conventional treatment with the tonic and attribute benefits to the tonic. The use of herbal formulas is a public health issue; thus, assessment of clinical benefit and potential interaction with *cancer treatment* is warranted.

BACKGROUND

Flor-Essence and Essiac are two of the most widely used herbal tonics by cancer patients. An estimated 35% of cancer patients in Canada 1 use these tonics, whose long and controversial history spans three decades.[2,3] In a recent survey at a large comprehensive cancer center in the United States, 38% of patients reported using herbs and overall, 4.9% used the Flor-Essence or Essiac tonic.[4] Both formulas contain four principal herbs: burdock root (*Arctium lappa L.*), Turkish rhubarb root (*Rheum palmatum L.*), sheep sorrel (*Rumex acetosella L.*), and slippery elm bark (*Ulmus rubra Muhl.*). However, Flor-Essence contains four additional herbs that are believed to potentiate the formula: watercress (*Nasturtium officinale R. Br.*), blessed thistle (*Cnicus benedictus L.*), red clover (*Trifolium pratense L.*) and kelp (*Laminaria digitata Lmx.*). Flor-Essence tonic is manufactured in Canada where approximately forty thousand units of tonic and dried herbs are distributed to Canada and the United States each month.

A review of the literature on these tonics and the four principal herbs resulted in 107 references. Of those, 68% (n=73) were related to cancer.[5] Although 24 pre-clinical evaluations of individual herbs were reported, no pre-clinical or clinical trials of the tonic were identified.[5] One clinical study with Essiac was discontinued by the Health Protection Branch of Health Canada in 1978 because of limited physician participation. Data from 87 participants was considered inadequate to determine any impact on survival.[2] However, no toxicity was reported, but quality of life or pain control were not evaluated.[3,6] Subsequently, claims for clinical benefit were discontinued by the manufacturers who then began marketing the product as a dietary supplement with general health claims (i.e., prevent disease, relieve pain, and improve quality of life).

Claims as a cancer cure persist, however, with anecdotal reports of reduced tumor growth, improved quality of life, and prolonged survival.[7] Although these tonics remain untested for anticancer activity, antioxidant activity has been confirmed for the Flor-Essence product.[8]

Moreover, qualitative thin layer chromatography (TLC) has confirmed seven herbs that contain trace elements, minerals, and phytoestrogens.[9] Levels of flavonoids, phenylcarboxylic acids, and emodin are monitored regularly in each batch.

Pre-clinical and clinical evaluations of Flor-Essence, in collaboration with the Russian Ministry of Health, have assessed acute and chronic toxicity. Acute toxicity studies were unable to determine a lethal dose in albino mice and rats. Furthermore, chronic toxicity tests found no renal or hepatic toxicity doses that were 10-fold the therapeutic dose (15 ml/kg) in albino mice and rats and 5-fold (7.5 ml/kg) in dogs.10 Sponsor initiated in vivo studies report reduced number and size of chemical mediated gastric ulcerations, protection of capillaries against xylene-mediated leakage, and prevention of chemically induced anti-inflammation.[9]

Given the historical and widespread use of these tonic, limited preclinical data by manufacturers only, and the anecdotal reports of efficacy from cancer patients, a pattern of use survey of Flor-Essence consumers and cancer patients was conducted to 1) profile the general consumers, 2) characterize cancer patients, and 3) determine their reasons for use, perceived benefits, and adverse events. Ultimately, this information will inform the medical community and cancer patients, stimulate manufacturers to prepare the tonics for clinical investigation with an Investigational Drug Application (IND), and guide the development of clinical trials with information about which cancer patients are more likely to use the product.

METHODS

Individuals who purchased Flor-Essence in the United States or Canada between June 1998 and August 1999 were invited to participate, regardless of age, gender, or disease status. The Committee for the Protection of Human Subjects at the University of Texas-Houston approved the study at two levels; participation was voluntary.

The manufacturers shipped 20,000 units of product in Canada and 65,245 in the United States over a three month period, beginning in June, 1998. Each product contained an invitation from the owner of Flora Manufacturing and Distributing Ltd. (Burnaby, B.C.) to participate so that the company could learn more about who is using the product and why. Each product contained a self-addressed, stamped postcard with the brief pattern of use survey. To ensure confidentiality, each postcard contained a unique identification number.

For Phase I, the pattern of use survey of general consumers collected information on demographics (i.e., age, gender, ethnicity, country of residence, marital status, education level, and household income), medical condition (i.e., arthritis, cancer, multiple sclerosis, or other), reasons for use (i.e., prevention, control symptoms, treat a medical condition, or other), duration of use, and perceived benefits using a 5-point rating scale from excellent to poor.

Current or former cancer patients were invited to call the University of Texas Center for Complementary and Alternative Medicine (UT-CAM) about the details of a second survey, specifically about their experience with the tonic. For Phase II, interested individuals who telephoned UT CAM and were current or former cancer patients were invited to participate. After obtaining verbal consent, research assistants collected contact information to mail the coded survey. Callers who declined to participate or who were ineligible were encouraged to complete and return the postcard. Flora Manufacturing and Distributing Ltd. provided one complimentary product to individuals who completed the cancer-specific survey.

The cancer-specific survey was adapted from an instrument that assessed complementary and alternative medicine (CAM) use in a comprehensive cancer center.[11] Cancer patients who were using the tonic provided information on their cancer status (i.e., date of diagnosis, stage and site of disease, current status), conventional treatment (i.e., chemotherapy, radiation, surgery, hormonal), and use of other CAM therapies. We also asked about their reasons and expectations for using Flor-Essence as well as information on dose, frequency, adverse events, positive effects, changes in symptoms (i.e., nausea, vomiting, loss of appetite, fatigue, pain). For patients who discussed use with their physicians, we asked how the physicians responded; otherwise, patients explained their reasons for nondisclosure about the herbal use.

Eligibility and consent rate
Of the 85,245 units distributed, 5,435 (response rate = 6.4%) postcards were received for Phase I. A total of 384 general consumers were excluded because they were treating pets (n = 38) or responded after the study closed (n = 346) in September, 1999. Of the 5,051 eligible general consumers, 3,749 (74.2%) were eligible for Phase II. Of these, 54.9% (n = 2,060) cancer patients consented to participate, and 1,588 (42.4%) completed the survey; however, 11 individuals were excluded because they responded after the study closed.

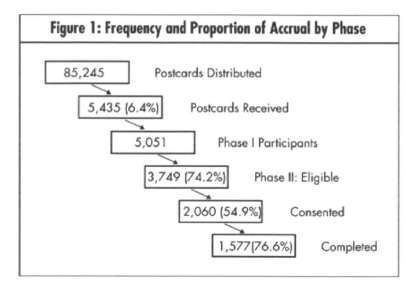

Figure 1: Frequency and Proportion of Accrual by Phase

Phase I: Profile of General Consumers
The majority of Flor-Essence consumers were educated above the high school level (63.6%), Caucasian (92.0%), married (68.8%), living in the United States (80.0%), 61.6 years of age (SD = 13.9), and approximately equally distributed by gender (Table 1.). The average duration of use was 15.79 months (SD = 17.35, range 0-130

months), and primarily (62.4%) to treat a medical condition rather than prevent disease (35.3%) or control symptoms (21.3%). Cancer was the most commonly reported medical condition (75.1%), but general consumers' other health conditions were arthritis (14.5%), multiple sclerosis (1.0%), and other (14.7%) conditions (i.e., allergies/ asthma, chronic fatigue, cysts, diabetes, high blood pressure/heart disease, hepatitis/liver disease, osteoporosis, or bladder, prostate, skin, or stomach problems). Most consumers rated the benefits of the tonic as very good/excellent (72.2%), but 24.4% rated the tonic as okay, and 3.4% as not very good/poor.

Table 1. Demographic Profile of Consumers & Cancer Patients				
	Consumers (n = 5,051)		Cancer Patients (n = 1,211)*	
Variable	**n**	**%**	**n**	**%**
Gender				
Women	2693	54.3	625	52.2
Men	2262	45.7	572	47.8
(Missing)	(96)	—	(14)	—
Ethnicity				
Caucasian	4511	92.0	1118	94.1
African-American	119	2.4	22	1.9
Asian	111	2.3	27	2.3
Hispanic	104	2.1	12	1.0
Other	59	1.2	9	.8
(Missing)	(147)	—	(23)	—
Marital status				
Married	3455	68.8	867	71.9
Widowed	554	11.0	120	10.0
Divorced	438	8.7	99	8.2
Single/never married	310	6.2	67	5.6
Living with partner	190	3.8	37	3.1
Separated	72	1.4	14	1.2
Other	2	0.0	2	0.2
(Missing)	(30)	—	(5)	—
Education				
High school or less	1790	36.4	427	36.1
Some college	1371	27.9	309	26.1
College graduate	995	20.3	268	22.6
Postgraduate study	756	15.4	180	15.2
(Missing)	(139)	—	(27)	—
Country of Residence				
United States	3895	80.0	941	79.9
Canada	976	20.0	237	20.1
(Missing)	(180)	—	(33)	—

*Surveys and postcards could not be matched to obtain demographic data for 366 cancer patients.
n = number

Phase II: Profile of Current and Former Cancer Patients

Demographics of Cancer Patients

Surveys and postcards were matched for 76.8% (n=1,211) of respondents in Phase I and II; thus, data on demographics were unavailable for 366 cancer patients. Flor-Essence was used equally by men and women, but most individuals were educated above the high school level (63.9%), Caucasian (94.1%), married (71.9%), living in the United States (79.9%), and 62.4 years of age (SD = 13.1) (Table 1).

Disease Status and Treatment Profile of Cancer Patients

Overall, 63.9% of cancer patients had been diagnosed over a 3-year period (i.e., 30.0% in 1998, 20.9% in 1997, 13.0% in 1996) for breast (22.0%), prostate (15.1%), or lung (10.6%) cancer. At the time of diagnosis, patients were equally distributed across stage I to IV disease; 33.7% reported metastatic disease. Of the 274 (19.0%) who reported "other" stage of disease at diagnosis, 49.8% did not know the stage. At the time of the survey, however, 38.9% of the respondents reported having no evidence of disease. Of the 365 (26.5%) who reported "other" stage of disease at the time of the survey, 58.6% did not know the stage (Table 2).

Table 2. Stages of Disease at Diagnosis and Time of Survey

	Time of Staging	
Stage of Disease	Diagnosis (%)	Survey (%)
I	24.3	8.9
II	18.8	6.1
III	19.0	6.4
IV	18.8	13.2
Other	19.0	26.5
No evidence of disease	N/A	38.9

At the time of their last check-up, 40.6% of participants stated they were told they had no evidence of disease. The remainder of participants stated their disease was regressing (14.6%), stable (13.9%), or progressing (15.5%); however, 9.9% did not know their disease status.

Most (88.7%) patients had received previous conventional cancer treatment, including surgery (51.4%), chemotherapy (46.6%), radiation therapy (36.7%), hormonal (15.1%), or other (11.3%) approaches. Of the 175 individuals who reported "other" approaches, 70.3% were CAM treatments. Therefore, 85.3% actually had received conventional treatment. At the time of the survey, most patients (60.9%) were currently being treated with the following: surgery (2.5%), chemotherapy (18.6%), radiation (3.4%), hormonal approaches (14.2%), or other therapies (29.9%). Of the 460 (29.9%) who reported receiving "other" therapies, 3.7% cited immune therapies while 90.2% were using CAM treatments. Therefore, only 36.8% actually were receiving conventional treatment at the time of the survey.

Duration of Use and Dose Information

At the time of the survey, almost all (98.3%) respondents were using Flor-Essence, and most (61.2%) had used the tonic for at least 6 months. Specifically, 44.7% had used the tonic for more than 12 months, 16.5% for 6 to 12 months, 32.7% for 1 month to less than 6 months, and 6.1% for less than one month.

Most patients (85.0%) reported that the instructions were adequate, but 15.0% stated that information was inadequate in general (n = 49) and specifically, inadequate regarding dose instructions (n = 39), duration of treatment (n = 31), and supporting research (n = 22). Overall, 30.4% (n = 475/1,551) reported following the recommended dose (i.e., 4 ounces or less daily). For the 1,079 patients who provided information on dose, 19.6% (n = 212) stated that they followed the instructions, but 12 individuals exceeded the recommended daily dose by using 4.5 to 10 ounces daily. Of the 867 patients (80.3%) who reported not following instructions, the majority (n = 756) actually followed the recommended guidelines, but 111 individuals exceeded the recommended dose by using 4.5 to 32 ounces daily. Thus, 11.4% (n = 123/1,079) of current or former cancer patients exceeded the recommended dose, but most (88.6%) followed the

Table 3. Compliance with Dose Instructions for Flor-Essence (n = 1,079)			
	Reported Following Dose Instructions		
Used Correct Dose (< 4 ounces/day)	Yes	No	Total
Yes	200	756	956
No	12	111	123
Total	212	867	1,079

Reasons for Use, Expectations, and Perceived Benefits and Adverse Events

Most cancer patients (84.9%) used the tonic because they believed it could help, and 23.7% because they were told that their cancer was incurable. Other reasons included the following: the tonic is nontoxic (56.4%), provides hope (50.4%), allows control over medical care decisions (39.8%), and other reasons (18.7%). Of the 294 who reported other reasons, the most common reasons were the recommendation by family or friends (34.6%) or belief in possible disease control (17.5%).

Most patients (76.5%) expected the tonic to improve their immune system, and others expected the tonic to improve survival (59.4%) or quality of life (53.2%), cure their cancer (48.9%), or relieve symptoms (28.6%). Of the 8.5% (n = 133) who cited other reasons, 63 expected Flor-Essence to control or prevent disease. The perceived benefits of the tonic reported by cancer patients were comparable to those of consumers since 75.5% of consumers were cancer patients. Cancer patients rated the benefits from very good/excellent (71.0%) and okay (27.1%) to not very good/poor (2.8%). Most patients (86.7%) reported positive effects, including the following: felt better (53.2%), no cancer progression (40.6%), able to carry out daily activities (34.0%), more energy (31.5%), coped better with the disease (26.3%), improved cancer symptoms (22.3%), and cured their cancer (16.2%).

Overall, 50.3% (n = 584/1162) reported an improvement in a symptom while using the tonic, including improvements in fatigue

(29.8%), appetite loss (15.0%), nausea (8.4%), pain (11.6%), vomiting (4.1%), and other symptoms (12.4%). However, 6.6% (n = 103/1560) reported ill effects with Flor-Essence. Overall, the most frequently reported adverse events were diarrhea (1.9%), constipation (1.2%), nausea (1.1%), and fatigue (0.9%).

Other Therapies and Disclosure to Providers
Most participants used CAM approaches simultaneously with the tonic including high dose vitamins and antioxidants (61.5%), other herbs and herbal mixtures (41.6%), special diets (41.4%), spiritual practices (35.0%), movement and physical therapies (21.5%), mind/body therapies (20.4%), and other CAM therapies (19.5%).

Most patients learned about this tonic from family and friends (65.1%), but other sources of information included books and magazines (35.1%), other cancer patients (18.4%), CAM practitioners (15.0%), doctors (4.3%), nurses (2.0%), social workers (0.2%), and other sources (14.6%). Of these 229 patients who learned of Flor-Essence from other sources, 55.9% were advised by health store personnel or nutritionists and 14.1% from the Internet.

Most patients (64.5%) discussed CAM use with their health care provider, and of those, 49.6% talked with their oncologists. Patients also discussed CAM use with their primary care physician (28.6%), nurse (13.1%), and social worker or psychiatrist (3.7%). During these discussions, patients perceived the providers to be either neutral (54.4%) or encouraging (40.5%). Few stated they were warned of risks (8.4%) or advised to discontinue the tonic (4.0%). Of the other responses cited (18.4%), participants reported that providers responded with "I don't believe in CAM" (n = 44) or "It probably won't hurt" (n = 36).

For the 559 patients who did not discuss CAM use with providers, the most common reasons were related to physicians: doctors never asked (62.3%), would discourage/disapprove (28.9%), or would not understand (26.7%). Others felt it was not important for physicians to be informed (25.0%) or were unsure if CAM was beneficial (11.9%). Only 5.9% believed that disclosure of CAM use resulted in the physician discontinuing the relationship.

DISCUSSION

This cross-sectional study is the first in North America to systematically assess the general pattern of use for Flor-Essence herbal tonic and specifically, to document the experience of cancer patients. This study found that consumers were predominately cancer patients, had used the tonic long term to treat a medical condition, and perceived the tonic as highly beneficial. Overall, they were predominately Caucasian, educated beyond high school and thus, characteristic of cancer patients who use CAM.[12-14] These patients in this survey were older and thus, not typical of cancer patients in general who use CAM,[15-25] although several studies report no association with age and CAM use.[13, 26-28] Most participants had been diagnosed with breast, prostate, or lung cancer, but approximately one-quarter were unaware of their disease stage at the time of diagnosis or the survey.

Although this convenience sample represents a self-selected group of cancer patients, over 60% had used the herbal mixture for greater than 6 months. The reasons for using the tonic were consistent with other surveys of cancer patients. Most patients use CAM approaches to gain hope and improve quality of life;[29] however, one-quarter turned to this CAM approach after learning their cancer was not curable.[23,30] We also found that many cancer patients combined the tonic with conventional treatment. The finding is consistent with the literature that indicates that few patients abandon conventional cancer care for CAM[14] whereas 60-80% combine CAM and conventional treatment.[12,13,18,19,24,27,29,31-35] The literature also suggests that physicians are interested[36,37] and willing to discuss CAM therapies with their patients, but want scientific evidence of efficacy and safety.[38] We found that most cancer patients discussed using the tonic with their physician; however, the majority who did not talk with physicians cited attitude of the physician as the primary reason for their nondisclosure.

Although several herbs have demonstrated anticancer, cytotoxic, and immunomodulatory activity,[9] clinical evidence to support the use of this agent is lacking as is data on possible interactions of Flor-Essence with conventional treatment. The majority of cancer patients reported following instructions; however, 11.4% were exceeding the recommended daily dose. In fact, 6.6% reported adverse events, including nausea, vomiting, and diarrhea. Of those who reported side effects, however, 11.8% reported that they exceeded the recommended daily dose. Despite the absence of scientific evidence, cancer patients expected the tonic to increase or improve the activity of their immune system, and many expected the tonic to improve survival and quality of life. The major sources of information were family, friends, and anecdotal reports.

Assessment of efficacy and safety by carefully controlled prospective clinical trials is critical. As a result of this pattern of use survey, a pilot study is planned to determine the feasibility of accruing patients who are presenting for palliative chemotherapy for Stage IV colon cancer to receive the herbal tonic or placebo. The pilot will provide experience in the context of integrated care to assess CAM. If successful, the preliminary data on quality of life, general health outcomes (i.e., pain, weight, and performance status), safety, and tolerability will provide the basis for a larger, more definitive trial. Such a study, however, would need sufficient power and long-term follow-up to determine efficacy using a full range of outcomes, including disease progression.

Limitations

As with all self-selected populations, this sample may be representative of more enthusiastic and committed consumers and thus, may be biased and not representative of the Flor-Essence consumer in general. However, these interesting results suggest the need for more representative samples. The response rate among eligible cancer patients was 42.4% and lower than rates for mailed surveys of CAM use among cancer patients in Italy (51.2%) and the United Kingdom (69%).[15,23] No study that we are aware of has attempted to conduct a pattern of use survey of CAM users by targeting consumers of an herbal product. Thus, we are unable to compare our response rate with those from similar studies.

CONCLUSION

This study confirmed that the widespread use of CAM is a reality and may reflect unmet patient needs within the current model of health care. These patients were clearly seeking hope and an opportunity to enhance their clinical outcome by expanding their treatment options. This behavior was reflected among general consumers as well. Since 1990, the prevalence of CAM use in the United States has increased to 42%, visits to CAM practitioners have risen to 629 million, and out-of-pocket expenditures climbed to $34.4 billion.39 In 1997, sales in the U.S. jumped 70% to $3.24 billion for herbs, and some $27 billion was spent in the U.S. on CAM therapies in general, with two-thirds of that money paid out-of-pocket.[39]

Regulatory requirements for the approval of prescription drugs require a review and analysis of clinical data for drug development, but botanicals differ from chemically produced drugs. These products are sold as dietary supplements rather than therapeutic agents. These herbal tonics consist of multiple herbs, each containing multiple constituents with known compounds, both active and inactive, as well as unknown compounds and elements, which may be active or inactive. The mechanism of action is usually unknown and variability within the same plant material usually high, thus challenging the ability for standardization and stability.[40] Regardless, the Flor-Essence tonic has a long history of sustained use over the past decades. Consumers believe they benefit from this product. Given the widespread use by cancer patients, regardless of clinical benefit, rigorous assessment by the conventional medical community is the next logical step to better inform patients and their physicians.

Correspondence and Reprint Requests to: Mary Ann Richardson, Dr.P.H., National Center for Complementary/Alternative Medicine, National Institutes of Health, 6707 Democracy Blvd, #106, Bethesda, Maryland 20892-5475; Phone: 301/402-1272; Fax: 301/480-3621; email: <marich@od.nih.gov>.

Acknowledgement to Thomas Greither, President of Flora Manufacturing Company for his collaboration and J. Fred Annegers, Ph.D., The University of Texas — Houston School of Public Health for assisting with the study concept and design. This study was supported by a grant from the National Institutes of Health (5 U24 CA66826-03) through the National Center for Complementary/Alternative Medicine and the National Cancer Institute and approved by the institutional review board at the University of Texas — Houston Health Science Center.

References

1. Gray RE, Fitch M, Greenberg M, et al. Perspectives of cancer survivors interested in unconventional therapies. *Journal of Psychosocial Oncology.* 1997;15:149-171.

2. Kaegi E. Unconventional therapies for cancer: 1. Essiac. *Canadian Medical Association Journal.* 1998;158(7):897-902.

3. Office of Technology Assessment (OTA). *Essiac.* Washington, D.C.: US Government Printing Office; 1990.

4. Richardson MA, Ramirez T, Palmer JL, Greisinger A, Singletary SE. Complementary/alternative medicine use in a comprehensive cancer center and the implications for oncology. *J Clin Oncol.* 2000;18:2505-2514.

5. The University of Texas Houston Center for Alternative Medicine Research in Cancer. Essiac summary. http://www.sph.uth.tmc.edu/www/utsph/utcam/agents/essiac/summ.htm.

6. Canadian Breast Cancer Research Initiative. 1999. Web Page. Available at: http://www.breast.cancer.ca.

7. National Research Council. Food Chemicals Codex. *Food and Nutrition Board, Division of Biological Sciences, Assembly of Life Sciences.* Washington, DC: National Academy Press; 1981.

8. Flora Manufacturing and Distributing Ltd. Flora company literature. Unpublished Data. 1996.

9. Tamayo C, Richardson MA, Diamond S, Skoda I. The chemistry and biological activity of herbs used in Flor-EssenceTM herbal tonic and Essiac™. *Phytotherapy Research.* 1999;13:1-14.

10. Flora Manufacturing and Distributing Files. Academy of Agricultural Sciences of the Russian Federation Research & Manufacturing Association. Research & Development Institute of Medical & Aromatic Plants. *Unpublished Report*. 1997.

11. Richardson MA, Ramirez T, Nanney K, Singletary SE. Alternative/complementary medicine: implications for patient-provider communication. *Proceedings of American Society of Clinical Oncology*. 1999;18:590A (abstr 2279).

12. Lerner IJ, Kennedy BJ. The prevalence of questionable methods of cancer treatment in the United States. CA *A Cancer Journal for Clinicians*. 1992;42:181-191.

13. Cassileth BR, Lusk EF, Strouse TB, Bodenheimer BJ. Contemporary unorthodox treatments in cancer medicine: a study of patients, treatments, and practitioners. *Annals of Internal Medicine*. 1984;101:105-112.

14. McGinnis LS. Alternative therapies, 1990. An overview. *Cancer*. 1991;67:1788-93.

15. Crocetti E, Crotti N, Feltrin A, Ponton P, Geddes M, Buiatti E. The use of complementary therapies by breast cancer patients attending conventional treatment. *European Journal of Cancer*. 1999;34(3):324-328.

16. Munstedt K, Kirsch K, Milch W, Sachsse S, Vahrson H. Unconventional cancer therapy–survey of patients with gynecological malignancy. *Archives of Gynecology and Obstetrics*. 1996;258:81-8.

17. Burstein HJ, Gelber S, Guadagnoli E, Weeks JC. Use of alternative medicine by women with early-stage breast cancer. *JAMA*. 1999;340:1773-1739.

18. Verhoef MJ, Hagen N, Pelletier G, Forsyth P. Alternative therapy use in neurologic diseases. *Neurology*. 1999;52:617-622.

19. Mottonen M, Uhari M. Use of micronutrients and alternative drugs by children with acute lymphoblastic leukemia. *Medical and Pediatric Oncology*. 1997;28:205-208.

20. Adler SR, Foskett JR. Disclosing complementary and alternative medicine use in the medical encounter: A qualitative study in women with breast cancer. *Journal of Family Practice.* 1999;48:453-458.

21. Begbie SD, Kerestes ZL, Bell DR. Patterns of alternative medicine use by cancer patients. *Medical Journal of Australia.* 1996;165:545-548.

22. Fisher P, Ward A. Complementary medicine in Europe. *British Medical Journal.* 1994;309:107-111.

23. Downer SM, Cody MM, McCluskey P, et al. Pursuit and practice of complementary therapies by cancer patients receiving conventional treatment. *British Medical Journal.* 1994;309:86-89.

24. Weis J, Bartsch H, Hennies F, et al. Complementary medicine in cancer patients: demand, patients' attitude, and psychological belief. Onkologie. 1998;21:144-149.

25. Risberg T, Lund E, Wist E, et al. The use of non-proven therapy among patients treated in Norwegian oncological departments: a cross-sectional national multicenter study. European Journal of Cancer. 1995;31A:1785-1789.

26. Sollner W, Zingg-Schir M, Rumpold G, Fritsch P. Attitude toward alternative therapy, compliance with standard treatment, and need for emotional support in patients with melanoma. *Archives of Dermatology.* 1997;133:316-321.

27. Grothey A, Duppe J, Hasenburg A, Voigtmann R. Use of alternative medicine in oncology. *Deutsche Medizinische Wochenschrift.* 1998;123(31-32):923-929.

28. Obrist R, von Meiss M, Obrecht JP. [The use of paramedical treatment methods by cancer patients. An inquiry on 101 ambulatory patients]. [German]. *Deutsche Medizinische Wochenschrift.* 1986;111:283-287.

29. Liu JM, Chu HC, Chin YH, et al. Cross-sectional study of use of alternative medicines in Chinese cancer patients. *Japanese Journal of Clinical Oncology.* 1997;27:37-41.

30. Hoey J. The arrogance of science and the pitfalls of hope. *Canadian Medical Association Journal.* 1998;159:803-804.

31. Jirillo A, Lacava J, Leone BA, Lonardi F, Bonciarelli G. Survey on the use of questionable methods of cancer treatment. Tumori. 1996;82:215-217.

32. Arkko PJ, Arkko BL, Kari-Kosinen O, Taskinen PJ. A survey of unproven cancer remedies and their users in an outpatient clinic for cancer therapy in Finland. *Social Science & Medicine – Medical Psychology & Medical Sociology.* 1980;14A:511-514.

33. Neogi T, Oza AM. Use of alternative medicine: are we failing in our communication with patients? A study assessing psychosocial impact of alternative medicine on cancer patients. *Proceedings of American Society of Clinical Oncology.* 1998;17:416A.

34. Fernandez CV, Stutzer CA, MacWilliam L, Fryer C. Alternative and complementary therapy use in pediatric oncology patients in British Columbia: prevalence and reasons for use and nonuse. *Journal of Clinical Oncology.* 1998;16:1279-1286.

35. Sawyer MG, Gannoni AF, Toogood IR, Antoniou G, Rice M. The use of alternative therapies by children with cancer. *Medical Journal of Australia.* 1994;160:320-322.

36. Berman B, Singh B, Hartnoll S, Singh B, Reilly D. Primary care physicians and complementary alternative medicine: training, attitudes, and practice patterns. *Journal of the American Board of Family Practice.* 1998;11:272-281.

37. Boucher T, Lenz S. An organizational survey of physicians' attitudes about and practice of complementary and alternative medicine. *Alternative Therapies in Health and Medicine.* 1998;4(6):59-65.

38. Crock R, Jarjoura D, Polen A, Rutecki G. Confronting the communication gap between conventional and alternative medicine: a survey of physicians' attitudes. *Alternative Therapies in Health & Medicine.* 1999;5(2):61-66.

39. Eisenberg DM, Davis RB, Ettner SL, et al. Trends in alternative medicine use in the United States, 1990-1997: results of a follow-up national survey. *JAMA*. 1998;280:1569-1575.

40. Lazarowych N, Pekos P. Use of fingerprinting and marker compounds for identification and standardization of botanical drugs: strategies for applying pharmaceutical HPLC analysis to herbal products. *Drug Information Journal*. 1998;32:497-512.

American Botanical Council, 6200 Manor Rd, Austin, TX 78723
Phone: 512-926-4900 | Fax: 512-926-2345
Website: www.herbalgram.org | Email: American Botanical Council

Reprinted from HerbalGram #50 (2000),
courtesy American Botanical Council
(www.herbalgram.org).

Testimonials

The following testimonials represent a sampling of the hundreds of letters received at Flora from appreciative patients who experienced a dramatic improvement in their health due to Flor·essence.

Breast cancer
June 2007

It has been five years since I was diagnosed with Stage 3 breast cancer. I have used conventional and alternative medicine.

Every doctor's report I have gotten has been better than good. I love Flor·essence tea. Every chance I get I tell people about it and what it has done for me.

Thank you very much for such a wonderful tea. It has been a blessing.

Sue H.
North Carolina

Breast cancer
April 2006

In 1994, my Grandmother was diagnosed with advanced stage IV breast cancer with numerous positive lymph nodes. They found cancer in her hip and back. Being a very active 67 year-old, this was devastating. She went through a radical mastectomy on her left side. She was given a chemo "pill" which left holes in her stomach and caused bleeding ulcers. She was then given IV chemotherapy only to experience convulsions on the way home. It nearly killed her. Her blood counts reached fatal numbers. She was even put on a feeding tube. She went from feeling fine to near death in a matter of a day. We were told to say good-bye—that she only had days to live.

My aunt had heard about the success of your Flo·essence Tea. They thought they would try it, since they had nothing else to lose. The doctors said it was quackery and disregarded any chance for her to recover. Well, they were wrong. She got better quite quickly. She took the tea everyday, my Grandfather brewing it for her faithfully. She was also on Tamoxifen. He couldn't believe her progress. Seven months later her cancer was gone. It was truly a miracle.

My Grandmother had a very small re-occurrence in her hip a few years later. When the doctors recommended chemotherapy, she refused, started the Tea again, and it went away. Her oncologist asked her if she had been treated somewhere else, she told him she was taking the Tea, and his words were, "Keep taking that Tea."

She lived another 10 years without cancer. We sadly lost her to a stroke in 2004. But, we would not have gotten another 10 years of such a wonderful Mother, Grandmother, and Wife if it wasn't for the Tea. We are so thankful. She is an inspiration to me.

Joette W.
Morton, WA

Throat and stomach cancer
November 1992

I am writing in regards to the Flor·essence herbal product and how it has turned my mother's health around.

On November 1991 my mother was diagnosed with cancer of the throat and stomach and given three months to live. On Boxing Day, my sister Vi heard about your herbal tea (Flor·essence) from her friend. She purchased some from you, brewed it up and made it available to Mom through the rest of the family. Mom was in bad shape; the doctor said she was too far gone for chemotherapy and prescribed morphine for the pain. He said, just try to keep her comfortable, that was all that can be done. Nobody was very enthusiastic about the herb tea, therefore, she didn't receive it on a regular basis, and she threw up much of that. She was thin as a rail and her eyes were dark sunken circles. She seemed oblivious of everything.

On May 16, an article on Flor·essence came out in the Vancouver Sun. There were several encouraging accounts on how the medicine had amazing results with other cancer patients. Our family became greatly enthusiastic about the medicine. My sister Barbara visited Mom for a while to see that she took the tea on a regular basis. As a result, Mom's health improved dramatically through the months. She gained weight; her appetite and mental capabilities came back.

Best of all, her doctor diagnosed her almost cancer free on or about October 1st, 1992.

Thank you, sincerely
William G.
Kamloops, BC

Prostate cancer
May 2007

I am 78 years old and have been remarkably healthy, which I attribute in part to the tea. I have been using Flor·essence Tea for 9 years. I mentioned in previous letters sent to your company that I have been using the tea in order to stop the spreading of my prostate cancer. I feel that the tea has reduced the spreading of my cancer, although the cancer has not been eliminated. I have not experienced any symptoms of the disease since my diagnosis 10 ½ years ago. My PSA did increase from 7.2 to 8.2 in the first two years of using the tea 9 years ago. This increase was much less than the 2 point increase that occurred during the 1 ½ year period from the time of my diagnosis.

In the last 6 years I have taken the tea regularly and my PSA is now at 0.2. I believe that the tea has helped to keep the cancer from returning. I also know that if I had started taking the tea before the age of 50, there is a good possibility that I never would have got cancer.

My wife showed a remarkable improvement in her general health after taking the tea regularly in 1999. Her arthritic pains completely disappeared. She previously had great difficulty sleeping, but she now only is awake when she goes to the bathroom once or twice a night. She has eliminated her constipation problems and her stomach discomfort. She appears much stronger and a whole lot more active. The side effects of her required medication have also decreased.

I regularly mentioned our experiences with the tea to relatives, friends and numerous other people, as well as writing to politicians and news-papers about the effectiveness of the tea. My wife and I plan to use the tea the remainder of our lives. It is a real shame that more people have not been exposed to the benefits of the tea. Because of the attitudes many doctors have toward herbal medication, it is sometimes difficult to convince people about the benefits of the tea. They are often cautioned about the use of alternative medicine, but they are seldom emphatically told about the serious side effects of many prescription drugs.
Sincerely,
Charles B.
Dunsmuir, CA

Bladder cancer
August 2003

I got up one morning and passed blood in my urine. My doctor who told me couldn't find anything wrong with me. One month later, around July 4, 1993, I passed blood again. Only this time, it was a lot of blood in my urine. I went to the hospital and learned I had multiple tumors in my bladder. The doctors told me I had stage 2 bladder cancer and that it had spread into the inside muscle layer of the bladder wall. It could've been worse but not much. Nevertheless, the doctors wanted to do surgery right away. They found three tumors which were removed. One was the size of a baseball and two were the size of golf balls.

Nine months later, I suffered my first recurrence. More tumors were surgically removed and I went on a bacterially based very harsh chemotherapy drug that is called Bacillus Calmette-Guérin (BCG), which burned off the inside of the bladder and urethra. The BCG didn't work. There was another recurrence and more surgery. And another. In total, I underwent surgery five times. Still, the cancer kept coming. After the fifth surgery, the tumors were found inside not only my bladder's membrane, but very close to the ureter from the right kidney. That was a very bad spot. My doctor told me I had two options. Either a sixth surgery or die. I looked at him and said, "I've had enough of this. I could be dead in six weeks. But I don't care anymore."

When you are diagnosed with bladder cancer at age 43 and experience more than five recurrences over the next five years and your doctor finally tells you there is nothing more that can be done, it is nice to be able to call yourself an old woodsman.

Five years clean, and I give credit to the cancer tonic Flor·essence from Flora. I began using it after I was proclaimed terminal, and it has contributed significantly to the disappearance of all signs of cancer.

Greg D.
Madison, CT

Skin cancer
November 2001

I wrote to you in 1998 about my experience with Flor·essence.
I'm still taking it but only about once a month. I will mix up a pkg.
and drink it once a day. I have never had another skin cancer since
I first heard of Flor·essence and started taking it in 1994.

My granddaughter who lives in Michigan called me about two years
ago to get information about my skin cancer "cure". A friend where
she works had cancer and after all the chemotherapy and other
treatments her doctors had given her six months to live. She started
on Flor·essence and now is feeling great. Her doctor said her cancer
is in "remission". She is very grateful and says she will never do
without her Flor·essence. She is now enjoying life and taking trips
with friends.

I am 91 years old, able to take care of myself, my home and do my
gardening and yard work. I haven't had a flu shot for over 11 years.
I can't remember when I had my last cold, at least 5 or 6 years ago.
I've been exposed to them many times. I was wondering if perhaps
it's due to Flor·essence? I am not on medication of any kind. I haven't
been to a doctor for at least two years. Do you think the tea has
made me immune? I occasionally get the sniffles from some-thing
blooming in my garden but never a cold.

I shall always be grateful to the stranger who told me about her
experience. I try to tell others but so many people are skeptical about
anything that isn't prescribed by a doctor. The woman in Michigan
told her doctor what she was taking. He said he had heard of it but
couldn't prescribe it. He tried to get her to take something else but
she refused.

I feel I owe my life to Flor·essence and Elaine Alexander.

Sincerely,
Gladys J.
California

Prostate cancer/diabetes
October 1998

On May 5, 1998 my PCP, Dr. Ronald Julia checked my prostate and suggested that I make an appointment with my oncologist, Dr. Camille Eyvazzadeh, for a more thorough exam. His diagnosis was "an extremely enlarged prostate". He sent me to a specialist on prostates, Dr. John Anderson, who suggested that I have an EKG and a PSA blood test. On May 22, 1998 the test was made at Tobyhanna Army Depot health Clinic. The results came back from the lab on June 9, 1998 at 48.7, 12 times higher than normal. Dr. Anderson personally called me for a consultation. On June 22, 1998 Dr. Anderson performed a biopsy on my prostate and discovered that it was completely filled with cancer. On July 10 and 13, 1998 he discovered cancer in my back rib on the left side and cancer in my seminole vesicle. On July 20, 1998 Dr. Anderson scheduled me for a consultation where he told me that he did not recommend surgery, and that he had been contacted by Dr. Eyvazzadeh, who told him that radiation was not possible because Dr. Eyvazzadeh had removed my colon in 1998 and re-sectioned my small intestine with a J-pouch. Radiation would destroy the pouch because of its proximity to the prostate and I would not survive the treatment. On July 24, 1998 Dr. Anderson gave me a one month chemotherapy shot and a prescription for Eulexin, a chemotherapy capsule. I took two capsules per day for 15 days and quit because of the side effects.

I began to drink Flor·essence, a blend of herbs in a tea form which I had learned about from my niece, Gail, who is into natural gardening of herbs, fruits, and vegetables. On Aug. 27, 1998 I received a three month chemotherapy shot from Dr. Anderson but no longer took the Eulexin capsules. I continued drinking the Flor·essence tea twice each day in four ounces of water and two ounces of liquid Flor·essence. On August 18, 1998 I had another PSA test with a 9.6 result. On Oct. 7, 1998 my third test result was 1.0. Praise the Lord, I am now healed of cancer. I then began testing my glucose twice each day to determine what Flor·essence might be doing for my diabetes. Before drinking the herbal tea my count was usually close to 200. My range was supposed to be from 94 to 133. After drinking the herbal tea as recommended, my count was 134, 133, 132, 131, 116, and 115. Praise the Lord again for these excellent test results. I am still on insulin until Dr. Julia also believes that I am healed of diabetes.

Charles G
Bethlehem, PA

Professional endorsement
March, 1996

This letter is intended as a professional appraisal of your company's product, Flor·essence. I have used this herbal formula on patients with a variety of degenerative health problems, including cancer, with excellent results.

The response of cancer patients, especially, when used with other therapeutic approaches, has been excellent. I have witnessed several cases of tumor regressions as well as major reductions in the side effects of chemo and radiation therapy in those persons who have used the product. Results have also been excellent in those individuals who have used your herbal product to the exclusion of other therapeutic modalities. Furthermore, during my lecture tours across Canada, I have had the chance of hearing the same kind of reports from consumers and professionals in every area of the country.

Of course, Flor·essence contains burdock (Arctium lappa) a plant that has undergone some credible research regarding its desmutagenic activity. As a matter of fact, a desmutagenic factor was isolated from burdock [Morita K Kada T Namiki M A desmutagenic factor isolated from burdock (Arctium lappa Linne). Mutat Res (1984 Oct) 129(1):25-31]. An earlier study had undertaken to establish the antitumor activity of burdock extracts: Dombradi CA Foldeak S Screening report on the antitumor activity of purified Arctium Lappa extracts. Tumori (1966 May-Jun) 52(3):173-5.

The effect of your product, however, is far greater than that of its individual constituents. All of which I have used, in a variety of combinations, with nowhere near the success I have had with Flor·essence. Of course, being well aware of your company's very high standards, I am also assured of the product's quality.

Because of the efficacy and safety of Floessence, I am pleased to recommend it wholeheartedly.

Sincerely yours in natural health,
Daniel-J. Crisafi, ND, MH, PhD
Granby, Quebec

Health References

Of the thousands of natural health products on the market, the following is a sampling of some of my personal favorites:

Nutritional and Herbal Supplements

Flora Inc.
For over 40 years, Flora has been preparing and providing award-winning, premium quality dietary supplements to the health consumer. Popular items include: Flor·essence, Udo's Choice 3·6·9 Oil Blend as well as Udo's Choice greens, digestive enzymes, probiotics and fiber blend, Floradix tonics, herbal extracts, healing teas and certified organic, cold-pressed seed oils.
805 E. Badger Road
Lynden, WA 98264
800-446-2110
www.florahealth.com

Flora Manufacturing & Distributing (Canadian affiliate)
7400 Fraser Park Drive
Burnaby, B.C. V5J 5B9
604-436-6000
www.florahealth.com

Pines International, Inc.
One of the original pioneers in preparing certified organic cereal grass products harvested at peek times from their own pristine farmlands in Kansas to guarantee maximum purity and potency.
PO Box 1107
1992 East 1400 Road
Lawrence, KS 66044
800-697-4637
www.wheatgrass.com

Aloe Life International
Offers high quality, polysaccharide-rich whole leaf aloe vera juice extracts for soothing digestion, immune support and other healing benefits.
4822 Santa Monica Avenue, Suite 231
San Diego, CA 92107
800-414-2563
www.aloelife.com

Maitake Products, Inc.
Manufacture a premium line of medicinal mushroom products, including Grifron Maitake D-Fraction for immune enhancement.
1 Madison Street, Suite F6
East Rutherford, NJ 07073
800-747-7418
www.maitake.com

Products for Healthy Home and Body

Bionaire
Leaders in air purification for over 20 years. Their air purifiers, humidifiers and dehumidifiers help maintain a fresher and cleaner home environment.
877-786-5742
www.filters2comfort.com

Plastaket Manufacturing Co.
Makers of one of the most durable and efficient juicers on the market. The Champion Juicer operates on the mastication method which extracts the juice by a chewing and pressing mechanism.
6220 E. Highway 12
Lodi, CA 95240
866-935-8423
www.championjuicer.com

BIOPRO Technology
Manufacture bio-energetic products (EMF Harmonizer cell chip) to counteract the electromagnetic field wave hazards of cell phones.
1905 Aston Avenue, Ste. 101
Carlsbad, CA 92008
866-999-2747
www.bioprotechnology.com

Dr. Hauschka Skin Care, Inc.
A full array of natural and premium quality skin, hair and sun care products made with organic and biodynamic plant ingredients.
20 Industrial Drive East
South Deerfield, MA 01373
800-247-9907
www.drhauschka.com

GAIAM Living
Natural products for the home including: organic cotton clothing, bedding and bath towels, water filtration systems, natural spectrum lighting, sound therapy as well as fitness and spa merchandise.
360 Interlocken Blvd., Ste. 300
Broomfield, CO 80021
www.gaiamliving.com

Seventh Generation, Inc.
A complete line of non-toxic and biodegradable household cleaning products, natural bath and feminine care items.
60 Lake Street
Burlington, VT 05401
800-456-1191
www.seventhgeneration.com

CANCER RESOURCE DIRECTORY

American Cancer Society
1599 Clifton Road NE
Atlanta, GA 30329-4251
800-227-2345
www.cancer.org
Nationwide agency providing free educational material and information on cancer, including statistics, treatment guidelines, community resources, diet, family counseling and other subjects.

Canadian Cancer Society
10 Alcorn Avenue, Suite 200
Toronto, Ontario M4V 3B1
416-961-7223
www.cancer.ca
A volunteer based organization which seeks to eradicate cancer and enhance the quality of life of cancer sufferers. Provides facts about cancer prevention, treatment and regional resource centers.

National Cancer Institute
Bethesda, MD 20892
800-422-6237
www.cancer.gov
Offers a wide range of information for people with cancer and their families, the public and health care professionals, including statistics, articles and recent clinical research updates.

**National Center for Cancer Complementary
and Alternative Medicine**
National Institutes of Health
9000 Rockville Pike
Bethesda, MD 20892
888-644-6226
www.nccam.nih.gov
Established in 1992 to scientifically investigate complementary and alternative cancer treatments, including mind-body medicine, biologically based therapies and holistic medical systems.

Y-Me National Breast Cancer Organization
212 W. Van Buren, Suite 1000
Chicago, IL 60607-3903
312-986-8338
Hotline 800-221-2141
www.y-me.org
A twenty-four hour hotline manned by breast cancer survivors
and offering information, empowerment and peer support so
that no one faces breast cancer alone.

REGIONAL:

Inspire Health
Integrated Cancer Care
1330 West 8th Avenue, Suite 200
Vancouver, B.C. V6H 4A6
604-734-7125
www.inspirehealth.ca
Non-profit organization providing an integrated whole
person approach to health and wellness for individuals living
with cancer.

Recommended Reading

A Course In Miracles. Foundation For Inner Peace. Glen Ellen, California, 1975

Airola, Paavo, PhD., ND., *Cancer-The Total Approach*. Phoenix: Health Plus Publishers, 1983

Balch, James and Phyllis. *Prescription For Nutritional Healing*. New York: Avery Publishing, 1990

Chopra, Deepak, M.D. *Perfect Health: The Complete Mind Body Guide*. New York: Harmony Books, 1990

Chopra, Deepak, M.D. *Quantum Healing-Exploring The Frontiers Of Mind/Body Medicine*. New York: Bantam Books, 1989

D'Adamo, Dr. Peter D. *Eat Right 4 Your Type*. New York: G. P. Putnam's Sons, 1996

Dyer, Dr. Wayne W. *Inspiration-Your Ultimate Calling*. Carlsbad, California: Hay House, Inc., 2006

Ehret, Arnold. *Mucusless-Diet Healing System*. Beaumont, California: Ehret Literature Publishing Co., 1972

Erasmus, Udo. *Fats That Heal, Fats That Kill*. Burnaby, Canada: Alive Books, 1986

Fischer, William. *How To Fight Cancer And Win*. Burnaby, Canada: Alive Books, 1987

Gawain, Shakti. *Creative Visualization*. New York: Bantam, 1983

Geffen, Jeremy, M.D. *The Journey Through Cancer*. New York: Three Rivers Press, 2000

Gerber, Richard, M.D. *Vibrational Medicine*. Santa Fe: Bear & Company, 1988

Gursche, Siegfried. *Healing With Herbal Juices* Burnaby, Canada: Alive Books, 1993

Haas, Elson, M.D. *Staying Healthy With Nutrition.* Berkeley, California, Celestial Arts, 1992

Hay, Louise. *You Can Heal Your Life.* Carlsbad, California: Hay House, 1999

Howell, Dr. Edward. *Enzyme Nutrition.* Wayne, New Jersey: Avery Publishing, 1985

Hutchens, Alma. *Indian Herbalogy Of North America.* Boston: Shambhala Publications, 1991

Jensen, Bernard. *Tissue Cleansing Through Bowel Management.* Escondido, California: Jensen Enterprises, 1981

Kubler-Ross, Elizabeth, M.D. *On Death And Dying.* New York: Scribner, 1969

Locke, S. and Colligan, D. *The Healer Within: The New Medicine Of Mind And Body.* New York: E.P. Dutton, 1986

McFarland, John Robert. *Now That I Have Cancer I Am Whole.* Kansas City: Andrews McMeel Publishing, LLC, 2007

Morrison, Judith. *The Book Of Ayurveda.* New York: Fireside-Simon & Shuster Inc., 1995

Murray, Michael, N.D. *The Complete Book Of Juicing.* New York: Three Rivers Press, 1998

Rama, Swami; Ballentine, Rudolph, M.D.; Hymes, Alan. *Science Of Breath.* Honesdale, Pennsylvania: The Himalayan International Institute, 1979

Reid, Daniel. *The Complete Book Of Chinese Health And Healing.* Boston: Shambhala Publications, 1995

Selye, Hans. *The Stress Of Life.* New York: McGraw-Hill Book Co., 1976

Shelton, Herbert. *Food Combining Made Easy.* San Antonio: Willow, 1982

Siegel, Bernie S., *M.D. Love, Medicine & Miracles.* New York: Perennial Library/Harper & Row, 1986

Silva, Jose. *The Silva Mind Control Method.* New York: Pocket Books, 1989

St. James, Elaine. *Inner Simplicity.* New York: Hyperion, 1995

Tierra, M. *The Way Of Herbs.* New York: Pocket Books, 1998

Walker, Norman, D.Sc., PhD. *Colon Health.* Prescott, Arizona: Norwalk Press, 1979

Wigmore, Ann. *The Hippocrates Diet.* Wayne, New Jersey: Avery Publishing Group Inc., 1984

Williamson, Marianne. *A Return To Love.* New York: Harper Collins Publishers Inc., 1992

About the Author

Gabriel Lightfriend has been involved in the natural health and healing movement for the past thirty years. *A Brighter Life* offers a vehicle for sharing his accumulated knowledge of nutritional foods, herbal remedies and the healing potential of our own thoughts.

Gabriel currently lives in the Pacific Northwest where he continues to pursue his love of writing and nature photography. For more information visit his website at:

www.gabriellightfriend.com

Also Available by Gabriel Lightfriend

Flowers of Light
Reflections of this Journey through Life

Flowers of Light is an enchanting tale that transports the reader to the timeless echo of a starlit canyon in the Arizona desert, to the enlightening herbal tea bar of a tiny coastal town in the Pacific Northwest and to an iridescent garden that so eloquently reflects the simple wisdom of nature. It is in these illuminating settings where an aging seeker encounters some philosophical companions who magically awaken his spirit and reverence for life.

www.flowerinspirations.com